The **OFFICIAL**

ONLY FOOLS *and* HORSES

Quiz Book

Splendid
BOOKS

The OFFICIAL ONLY FOOLS and HORSES Quiz Book

Compiled by
Dan Sullivan and Jim Sullivan

Foreword by John Sullivan

Published in 2010 by Splendid Books Limited

Copyright © 2010 Dan Sullivan and Jim Sullivan

The rights of Dan Sullivan and Jim Sullivan to be identified as the Authors
of the work has been asserted by them in accordance with the Copyright,
Designs and Patents Act 1988.

Splendid Books Limited
The Old Hambledon Racecourse Centre
Sheardley Lane
Droxford
Hampshire
SO32 3QY

www.splendidbooks.co.uk

ISBN: 9780955891663

Designed by Design Image Ltd.
www.design-image.co.uk

Printed and bound in the UK by CPI Mackays, Chatham ME5 8TD

Every effort has been made to fulfil requirements with regard to
reproducing copyright material. The writers and publisher will be glad
to rectify any omissions at the earliest opportunity.

Photographs:
Radio Times
'Nelson Mandela House' photograph courtesy of Rick Weston

☆★ CONTENTS

Regular cast and key production team

REGULAR CAST
Del Trotter – David Jason
Rodney Trotter – Nicholas Lyndhurst
Grandad Trotter – Lennard Pearce
Uncle Albert – Buster Merryfield

KEY PRODUCTION TEAM
John Sullivan - **Writer**

Producers:
Ray Butt (1981-87); Gareth Gwenlan (1988-2003)

Directors:
Martin Shardlow (1981), Bernard Thompson
('Christmas Crackers'); Ray Butt (1982, 1983, 'Video
Nasty', 'Who Wants to be a Millionaire?', 'To Hull
and Back', 'The Royal Flush', 'The Frog's Legacy');
Susan Belbin (1985); Mandie Fletcher (1986); Tony
Dow (1988-2003); Gareth Gwenlan ('Miami Twice
(part 1) – The American Dream')

When my sons, Dan and Jim, decided to write this "Official" *Only Fools and Horses* Quiz Book my initial reaction was "What a great idea, why didn't we think of it years ago?" But then we wouldn't have had so many episodes and therefore so many interesting and challenging questions. So it made sense.

I've read the questions, all 1015 of them, and there's such a great range in the levels of difficulty. There are some that possibly children might get right and others that only true aficionados would stand a chance with. I have to admit that every so often one of them would stump me. But, then again, I wrote some of the scenes and characters mentioned in the book 30 years ago, so it's not that surprising the old grey matter failed me on a few occasions. But having said that, at one point I was actually getting so many questions right I was feeling quite proud of myself and my memory, until I realised that because I was in the middle of writing the next two "*Rock & Chips*" Specials (the 1960s prequel to OFAH) I had been going over all my old 'Fools' scripts researching Trotter mythology.

Some of the most difficult questions I came across aren't even asked in the book. Things like characters names – where did I get the name Young Towser? And where did Ugandan Morris come from? Well, Uganda obviously, but you know what I mean. Some of the names mentioned; Alfie Flowers, Tommy Razzle, Lenny Corby and a few more, were guys who lived in my street. I never actually met Sunglasses Ron but south London legend had it that he lived in the Wolfie Smith country of Tooting. But over the years many people from different areas, and even cities, have claimed to have known Sunglasses Ron, he seems to have been everywhere – I now see him as a modern Kilroy and expect to see signs written on walls boasting "Sunglasses Ron Woz Here".

And the same goes for various incidents. Things such as the chandelier crashing to the ground was a true event that happened to my father back in the early 1930s when he was an apprentice. The same goes for Del's fall through the bar – an incident I witnessed in a pub called The George at the top of Balham Hill. I can remember meeting David Jason in the BBC Club and telling him about it. We were both so desperate to do it in 'Fools' but it took fully ten years for the right moment to arrive – but arrive it did, thank God! But there are so many other moments in this book that made me wonder where they came from. Like the Jolly Boys' Outing to Margate and their coach blowing up; Del hang-gliding off of a cliff and flying out to sea; the three-wheeled van shooting over a hill and momentarily flying along the public-highway like Steve McQueen in "*Bullit*", the famous blow-up dolls and many more besides. When I was younger I went on a couple of beanos, both to Southend, but they were pretty uneventful journeys and both times our coach came back in one piece. I've never hang-glided and never wished to, and I've never driven a car fast enough to actually leave the ground – and I've never seen a blow-up doll – honest.

As a writer 90% of the action and dialogue in my scripts is pure imagination, the true incidents and lines are bonuses, but I often look back on some of the moments mentioned above and wonder whether something happened way back in the mists of time that caused me to write them. Perhaps I'll never know and perhaps I should be grateful for that.

At times, during the 22 years of writing the OFAH saga, and indeed life in general, I came across moments where bitter disappointment merely concealed wonderful opportunities. Such was the case with the notorious Driscoll Brothers. I had mentioned them in an early script as Peckham's version (albeit a very stupid version) of the Kray Twins and the Richardson Brothers (who also lived in my street). But although the Driscolls existed (in name only) I had no plans to actually introduce them in the series. But one evening I was watching the Terry Wogan chat show and his guest was the brilliant actor Anthony Hopkins (now Sir Ton').

At the end of the interview TW asked him if he had any ambitions left and the Hollywood legend uttered the immortal words "Yes, I would love to play a part in *"Only Fools and Horses"*. I didn't sleep that night, I didn't even go to bed. I sat in my office and wrote scenes and a story for the Driscoll Brothers with Anthony Hopkins playing Danny Driscoll.

The next day I phoned his London agent and said tell AH his prayers have been answered and I've got a great part for him in OFAH. But later that afternoon I had a call back to say that Anthony was unavailable for our recording dates as he would be busy in Los Angeles filming something called *"The Silence of the Lambs"*. That was a real disappointment and I had the added problem of being left with a plot and almost a whole script heavily involving the Driscoll Brothers which I now had to recast. And who could compare with Anthony Hopkins? But the following day John Challis (Boycie) called to say that one of his actor pals would love to be in 'Fools'; the actor turned out to be the wonderful Roy Marsden (Detective Adam Dalgliesh; just one of his great roles) and we immediately offered him the part of Danny Driscoll. Then came another call to say that an actor I had wanted to work with for ages, Chris Ryan (*The Young Ones*), was available to play Tony Driscoll. So disappointment turned to triumph – if Anthony Hopkins hadn't mentioned he was a "Fools" fan I may never have written the Driscoll Brothers into the series; indeed they went on to star in three episodes of the 'Fools' spin-off "*The Green Green Grass*". And I now couldn't imagine any other actors playing those roles.

Well, these have been a few of my rather rambling recollections of the series. If they haven't actually helped you with the answers I hope they may have whetted your appetite for the pages ahead. If you play the quiz as an individual or part of a team, or as a family game, I hope it gives you lots of fun and, like me, rekindles some warm memories.

Good luck and bonnet de douche to all.

John Sullivan

SERIES
★ ★ ★ ★ ★ ★ ★ ★ ★ ★
ONE

SERIES ONE EPISODE GUIDE

Episode 1: Big Brother

After a row with Del, Rodney abandons the high flying world
of market trading and runs away to see the world. But it's
not long before he starts to miss Peckham and returns home.
Forgetting to take his passport with him didn't help either.

First screened: Tuesday September 8th 1981 at 8.30pm.

Episode 2: Go West Young Man

Del and Rodney enter the second hand car market with a
vehicle that literally goes like a bomb. But after a night out on
the town the car comes back to bite them.

First screened: Tuesday September 15th 1981 at 8.30pm.

Episode 3: Cash and Curry

Del is swooping in on the deal of a lifetime – one which could
keep them all in pilau rice forever. But he hasn't reckoned on
a touch of Indian style gang warfare.

First screened: Tuesday September 22nd 1981 at 8.30pm.

Episode 4: The Second Time Around

When Del's old flame, and Achilles heel, Pauline, returns from
America, the fire is quickly rekindled. Unfortunately for Del,

Rodney and Grandad are on hand to make sure the course of true love runs anything but smooth.

First screened: Tuesday September 29th 1981 at 8.30pm.

Episode 5: A Slow Bus To Chingford
When Del cuts a deal that sees him getting the use of an open topped bus, he spots the opportunity to make money… but not if a conniving Grandad has anything to do with it.

First screened: Tuesday October 6th 1981 at 8.30pm.

Episode 6: The Russians Are Coming
When Del manages to get his hands on three tons of lead and an instruction manual, the Trotters start making preparations for World War 3!

First screened: Tuesday October 13th 1981 at 8.30pm.

Episode 7: Christmas Crackers
The season of good cheer is upon the family, but Del and Rodney are dreading the gastronomic nightmare that is Grandad's Christmas lunch. Sick of their moaning, Grandad decides to go to an old folks do, whilst Del and Rodney decide to hit the only night club that is open on Christmas night.

First screened: Monday December 28th 1981 at 9.55pm.

Quiz One - Series One

1. In the opening scene of *Big Brother* how many television sets is Grandad watching?

a) 2 **b)** 3 **c)** 4 ....

2. In *A Slow Bus To Chingford* what is the name of Del's open top tourist bus service?

....

3. In which borough of London does Del plan to take his tourists on a 'walkabout'?

....

4. In *Cash and Curry* what does Del claim to be a black belt in?

....

5. In *Go West Young Man* Rodney reveals that he has a 'thing' for what?

....

6. According to Grandad, which Hollywood actor "always plays the black fella"?

....

7. Which actor, as Del points out, is Grandad actually referring to?

....

8. In *Second Time Around* what is the surname of Del's ex fiancée, Pauline?

....

9. According to Pauline she has recently been living in which American city?

a) Los Angeles   **b)** San Francisco   **c)** Las Vegas   ....

10. How many husbands of Pauline have died?

a) 1   **b)** 2   **c)** 3   ....

11. What was the full name of Pauline's first husband?

....

12. In *Go West Young Man* what is the name of the exotic cocktail Del orders in the first nightclub he and Rodney go to?

....

13. What drink does Rodney order?

....

14. In the opening scene of *Cash and Curry* Rodney turns up in the three-wheel van, but what car does he drive away in?

....

15. In *A Slow Bus To Chingford* what is the name of Rodney's new girlfriend?

....

16. What item of clothing does she claim she is not wearing?

....

17. She has a brother who paints for the council. What is his name?

....

18. In *Christmas Crackers* Del claims that any woman going out with him is guaranteed what type of meal?

a) A ruby murray   **b)** A steak meal   **c)** A fish supper ....

19. In *Big Brother* what is the name of the Nag's Head barmaid Del refers to as "a bit of an old dog"?

....

20. In *Cash and Curry* Mr Ram claims that Kuvera is the Hindu God of what?

a) Wealth   **b)** Love   **c)** Happiness ....

21. What did Del think Kuvera was?

....

22. In *The Russians Are Coming* what does Rodney claim Del tried to sell to the Brixton rioters?

....

23. In *Big Brother* what does Del buy off Trigger that he ends up chucking in the river?

....

24. In *Christmas Crackers* what make of pen has Del given Rodney as a present?

a) Parker   **b)** Replay   **c)** Bic ....

25. In *Big Brother* what does Del try to force-feed Grandad with?

....

26. In *Cash and Curry* how much do Del and Rodney pay for the statue of Kuvera?

a) £1,000   **b)** £2,000   **c)** £3,000 ....

27. How much do they discover it is really worth?

....

17

The Official Only Fools and Horses Quiz Book

28. In *Christmas Crackers* what is the name of the club that Del and Rodney go to on Christmas night?

a) The One-Eleven Club
b) The Monte Carlo Club
c) The Down By The Riverside Club ....

29. In the club they bump into a friend of Del's who is very depressed. What is his name?

....

30. What drug does Del recommend for his friend's hospitalised dad?

a) Penicillin b) Aspirin c) Antibiotics ....

31. In *Big Brother* what nickname does Del use when referring to Rodney's girlfriend at art college?

....

32. Where was she deported to?

....

33. According to Del how long was Rodney at art college before he was expelled?

....

18

34. In *Go West Young Man* what is unusual about the two women sitting at the bar that Del tries to pull?

....

35. In *Second Time Around* what does Pauline hide from Grandad?

....

36. What was Pauline's previous job?

....

37. According to Del, what did Pauline's mum work as?

....

38. What type of insurance does Pauline encourage Del to take out?

....

39. To get revenge on Del, Pauline calls which country's talking clock?

a) Australia **b)** Canada **c)** America ....

40. In *Big Brother* what game does Grandad try to play on a talking chess board?

....

41. In *A Slow Bus To Chingford* Del mentions a dream he had in which he stands beneath what neon-lit, fifty foot high, three letter word?

....

42. In *Christmas Crackers* what does Grandad forget to remove from the turkey before cooking it?

....

43. What is missing from the electric knife that Del carves the turkey with?

....

44. In *The Russians Are Coming* where does Grandad originally suggest they build their nuclear fallout shelter?

....

45. Where do the Trotters eventually build it?

....

46. In *Big Brother* where does Grandad say that Rodney is hitch-hiking to after a row with Del?

....

20

47. Where in London is the doss house that Rodney confesses to have really been staying?

....

48. What is the name of the doss house?

....

49. In *Go West Young Man* what does Del hide in his garage for Boycie?

....

50. In *The Russians Are Coming* Grandad mentions a brother who fought in World War One. What was his name?

....

51. In *Go West Young Man* what does Rodney claim he has never smoked?

....

52. In *A Slow Bus To Chingford* Del gets Rodney a job as a N.S.O. What does N.S.O. stand for?

....

The Official Only Fools and Horses Quiz Book

53. What kind of uniform does Rodney wear for his new job?

a) Policeman's uniform
b) Traffic warden's uniform
c) Bus conductor's uniform ....

54. In *Big Brother* what is the name of the English girl Rodney claims to have met in St. Tropez?

....

55. In *Go West Young Man* what is the nickname of the Australian Del sells a dodgy Cortina to?

....

56. In *Christmas Crackers* what is the full title of the book that Rodney is reading?

....

57. Who lent him the book?

....

58. In *Cash and Curry* what nickname does Del give to the Indian heavy who confronts him in the car park?

....

59. According to Del which famous renaissance artist was a "wally brain"?

a) Michelangelo **b)** Leonardo da Vinci **c)** Raphael ....

60. In *A Slow Bus To Chingford* Del gets Rodney a guard dog. What is the dog's name?

....

61. In *Big Brother* what have the Trotters bought that only have one leg?

....

62. In the opening scene of *Go West Young Man* Rodney is moping over a girl who, according to Del, has fat thighs. What is her name?

....

63. Who does Del claim to have seen her dancing with at the Nag's Head disco the night before?

....

64. In *The Russians Are Coming* what are the Trotters doing a dummy run of when they are stopped by the police?

....

65. What is the name of the policeman who pulls them over?

....

66. What is the name of the policeman's siren happy partner?

....

67. In *Go West Young Man* Del attempts to impress two female night clubbers by claiming that Rodney does what for a living?

....

68. What nickname does Del claim the sporting press have given Rodney?

....

69. What does Del write the girls phone numbers on that Rodney throws out the car window?

....

70. In The opening scene of *Second Time Around* what does Rodney ask Del to bring him back from the pub?

....

71. In *A Slow Bus To Chingford* where does Del find the leaflets that Grandad was supposed to distribute?

....

72. In *Second Time Around* Trigger phones Del to tell him that Pauline's first husband died of what?

....

73. In *Go West Young Man* who crashes into the Trotters?

....

74. In *Cash and Curry* what is the full name of Mr Ram's supposed rival?

....

75. In *Second Time Around* which 'relative' do the Trotters go to stay with?

....

76. In which seaside resort does she live?

a) Southend **b)** Bognor **c)** Clacton ....

77. In *Second Time Around*, what, to their annoyance, does Pauline get Rodney and Grandad for dinner?

....

78. In *The Russians Are Coming* what does Rodney suspect is trying to nest in their air filter?

....

79. According to Del, how long did Rodney's hunger strike, in protest of American missiles, last?

....

80. In *Christmas Crackers* what, to Rodney's annoyance, is on two TV channels?

a) A Bond film
b) Songs of Praise
c) The circus ....

★ ★ ★

SERIES
★★★★★★★★★★
TWO

SERIES TWO EPISODE GUIDE

Episode 1: The Long Legs Of The Law
Del and Grandad's peaceful evening in front of the TV is obliterated when Rodney brings his new date, Sandra, back to the flat.

First screened: Thursday October 21st 1982 at 8.30pm.

Episode 2: Ashes To Ashes
When Trigger's gran dies, the Trotters offer their support by agreeing to sell off some of her old possessions, but before long they also find themselves responsible for finding a final resting place for Trigger's late grandad's remains.

First screened: Thursday October 28th 1982 at 8.30pm.

Episode 3: A Losing Streak
Del's pride gets the better of him when Boycie challenges him to a winner takes all poker match. Thinking he is triumphant and about to collect his winnings, Boycie realises at the last minute that you can't cheat a cheater.

First screened: Thursday November 4th 1982 at 8.30pm.

Episode 4: No Greater Love....
Rodney has lost his heart to a mature woman, but is he man enough to stand up to her ultra violent, and soon to be

released, jailbird husband? Luckily for him, Del is on hand to clear the path for true love.

First screened: Thursday November 11th 1982 at 8.30pm.

Episode 5: The Yellow Peril

Del arranges for Rodney and Grandad to paint the kitchen of a local Chinese take-away, whilst doing a spot of secret decorating himself. Unfortunately the hooky paint they use doesn't come with labels.

First screened: Thursday November 18th 1982 at 8.30pm.

Episode 6: It Never Rains....

It's holiday time and the Trotters head to Spain. But while Del and Rodney are soaking up the sun, Grandad finds himself in a prison cell and with a lot of explaining to do.

First screened: Thursday November 25th 1982 at 8.30pm.

Episode 7: A Touch Of Glass

After Del worms his way into a grand stately home, the Trotters go into the chandelier cleaning business. What could possibly go wrong?

First screened: Thursday December 2nd 1982 at 8.30pm.

The Official Only Fools and Horses Quiz Book

Episode 8: Diamonds Are For Heather
When Del catches the eye of the lovely Heather, it looks like he just might have found the future Mrs Trotter. One small problem though: her husband.

First screened: Thursday December 30th 1982 at 7.55pm.

☆ ☆ ☆

QUIZ TWO - SERIES TWO

1. In *The Long Legs Of The Law* what has Grandad misplaced that Del finds out by the rubbish chute?

a) His hat   **b)** His teeth   **c)** His money belt   ....

2. In *A Losing Streak* what is the name of Del's homemade perfume?

....

3. In *It Never Rains* where do the Trotters go for their holiday?

a) Tenerife   b) Magaluf   c) Benidorm   ....

4. What does Grandad cook to get them into the holiday spirit?

a) Paella   **b)** Spanish omelette   **c)** Gazpacho   ....

5. In *A Touch Of Glass* what is the name of the stately home where the Trotters try their hand at chandelier cleaning?

....

6. In the drawing room of the stately home, Del admires a painting by which artist?

a) Donatello   **b)** Canaletto   **c)** Boticelli   ....

The Official Only Fools and Horses Quiz Book

7. What is the name of the stately home's snooty butler?

a) Patterson **b)** Jones **c)** Wallace ....

8. In *Diamonds Are For Heather* what song does Del request that empties the Nag's Head?

....

9. According to Del, Tommy Razzle and who else teamed up to go into the false ceiling business?

a) Monkey Harris **b)** Towser **c)** Paddy The Greek ....

10. In *Diamonds Are For Heather* which of Del's associates does he get an engagement ring from?

....

11. In the opening scene of *Ashes To Ashes* what is Del selling in the market?

....

12. In *A Losing Streak* how does Rodney offer to raise stake money for Del's poker game?

....

13. How much money does Rodney raise?

....

14. In *The Yellow Peril* what is the name of the Chinese restaurant that the Trotters redecorate?

....

15. What is the name of the restaurant's manager?

a) Mr Chin **b)** Mr Lee **c)** Mr Chan ....

16. What colour is the restaurant manager's first choice for his kitchen?

a) Green **b)** White **c)** Blue ....

17. What colour do the Trotters actually paint it?

....

18. Who did Del buy the paint from?

....

19. In *The Long Legs Of The Law* what is the name of the cafe Del and Rodney go to?

a) Old Oak Cafe
b) Royal Oak Cafe
c) Burnt Oak Cafe ....

The Official Only Fools and Horses Quiz Book

20. Whilst there, Del eats a massive breakfast. Which of the following does he **not** order?

a) Chips **b)** Mushrooms **c)** Fried slice ....

21. What is the name of the cafe's owner?

....

22. In *It Never Rains* what is the name of the hotel the Trotters stay at?

....

23. What is the name of Trigger's late gran?

....

24. In *No Greater Love* how old is Rodney's new girlfriend, Irene?

a) 40 **b)** 45 **c)** 50 ....

25. How old does Rodney say he is when Irene asks him?

....

26. What is Irene's husband's full name?

....

27. According to Rodney what prison is Irene's husband in?

....

28. Which of the following is he **not** in prison for?

a) GBH **b)** Wounding with intent **c)** ABH ....

29. In *It Never Rains* what language does Del attempt to use when trying to chat up a woman by the pool?

a) Spanish **b)** French **c)** German ....

30. What is the woman's name?

a) Julie **b)** Jenny **c)** Jackie ....

31. In *Diamonds Are For Heather* what brand of washing powder has Del got himself lumbered with?

a) Daz **b)** Persil **c)** Ariel ....

32. In *The Long Legs Of The Law* Rodney gets a date with a woman named Sandra. What is her profession?

a) Lollypop lady
b) Traffic warden
c) Policewoman ....

33. In *The Yellow Peril* Del and Rodney visit their mum, Joan's, grave. On Joan's headstone, what date is given for her death? (day, month and year)

....

34. What makes Joan's monument so unique?

....

35. In what year was Grandad deported from Spain?

a) 1929   **b)** 1932   **c)** 1936 ....

36. What was he deported for?

....

37. In *The Long Legs Of The Law* what was the title of the film Rodney took Sandra to see?

....

38. Including Trigger, how many people attend his gran's funeral?

a) 4   **b)** 5   **c)** 6 ....

39. In the opening scene of *A Losing Streak* Del is on the phone to Winston. What is he trying to sell him?

....

40. In *A Touch Of Glass* the chandelier the Trotters smash dates back to which French king?

a) Louis 12th
b) Louis 13th
c) Louis 14th ....

41. In *The Long Legs Of The Law* what 'Police' record does Del claim Rodney has?

....

42. In *A Losing Streak* what type of coin does Grandad give to Del?

....

43. What was the profession of Trigger's grandad Arthur?

....

44. Who did Arthur suspect his wife was having an affair with while he was away in the army?

....

45. Where does Del hide the emergency money that Joan left him and Rodney?

....

46. How much money is it?

a) £500
b) £750
c) £1,000 ....

47. In *Diamonds Are For Heather* what is the name of Heather's estranged husband?

....

48. According to Heather he has got a new job as a what?

....

49. In *A Losing Streak* who do both Del and Trigger claim that "all the lads remember"?

....

50. In *The Long Legs Of The Law* what drink does Del 'accidentally' spill over Sandra's watch?

a) Martini
b) Singapore sling
c) Gin and Tonic ....

51. Besides taking her to the pictures, buying her a packet of cashew nuts and giving her a stolen watch, what other gift does Rodney spoil Sandra with?

a) A Big Mac meal
b) A Doner kebab
c) Rock and Chips ....

52. In *Ashes To Ashes* where does Trigger say he is going on holiday to 'live it up a bit'?

....

53. In *No Greater Love* Rodney has a romantic telephone conversation. Who does he tell Del he was talking to?

....

54. In *Diamonds Are For Heather* what is the stage name of the brothers who provide the Flamenco style entertainment for the Nag's Head Spanish night?

a) The Magaluf Brothers
b) The Marbella Brothers
c) The Benidorm Brothers ....

55. In *Ashes To Ashes* what does the sign on the Trotter's bathroom door read?

....

56. In *Diamonds Are For Heather* what is the name of Heather's mature student babysitter?

....

57. In *Ashes To Ashes* what does Del speak into pretending to be the ghost of Trigger's grandad?

....

58. In *A Touch Of Glass* Del has bought a consignment of musical china cats that play which song?

....

59. In which town was the antique shop where Del bought them?

a) Exeter   **b)** Yeovil   **c)** Bath   ....

60. Where were the china cats made?

a) Taiwan   **b)** Cambodia   **c)** North Korea   ....

61. In *A Losing Streak* what does Trigger give Del so that Del can continue playing the poker game?

....

62. In *Ashes To Ashes* where does Grandad suggest they scatter Trigger's grandad's ashes?

....

63. What 'hymn' does Rodney suggest he and Del sing as they scatter the ashes?

....

64. In *No Greater Love* what is Irene's punk rocker son called?

....

65. What TV channel does Del say that Irene's son could pick up on his hair?

a) BBC 2 **b)** ITV **c)** Channel 4 ....

66. In *A Losing Streak* what is Del's winning hand?

....

67. At the end of *No Greater Love* Rodney has a new girlfriend. What is her name?

....

68. Where did he meet her?

....

69. In *The Yellow Peril* Grandad worriedly claims that Joan's newly brightened up monument is in the main flight path of which airport?

a) Heathrow
b) Luton
c) Gatwick   ....

70. In *Diamonds Are For Heather* in what part of London does Heather live?

....

71. In *Ashes To Ashes* at which dock does Del choose to perform a burial at sea?

....

72. What other mode of disposal does Del consider for the ashes?

....

73. According to Grandad he was once held in a prison close to which Spanish town?

a) Cadiz   b) Tarifa   c) Malaga   ....

74. In *Diamonds Are for Heather* what does the playground caretaker tell Del off for?

....

75. In *Ashes To Ashes* what is to blame for Trigger being stuck at Gatwick airport?

a) Snow   **b)** Fog   **c)** Volcanic ash   ....

76. At the end of *A Losing Streak* Del offers Boycie a chance to win some money back by tossing a coin. What does Rodney call?

....

77. According To Rodney's deep sea diver's watch, where is it nearly chucking out time?

a) New Delhi   **b)** Peking   **c)** Dubai   ....

78. In *Diamonds Are For Heather* what is the name of Heather's baby son?

a) Darryl   **b)** Darren   **c)** Danny   ....

79. In *It Never Rains* what is Grandad arrested for?

....

80. In *Diamonds Are For Heather* what do a smooching Del and Heather get thrown out of?

a) Zoo   **b)** Museum   **c)** Planetarium   ....

★ ★ ★

SERIES
★★★★★★★★★
THREE

SERIES THREE EPISODE GUIDE

Episode 1: Homesick
With the lift out of action again, the stairs have become too much for poor old Grandad. If only they could move into one of those nice, new, council built bungalows. Over to Rodney - the new chairman of the housing committee.

First screened: Thursday November 10th 1983 at 8.30pm.

Episode 2: Healthy Competition
Rodney asserts his independence and decides to leave Del's side and go it alone in the world of trading. A week later and it's pretty clear that his business skills could use some tweaking and he wants his old partner back.

First screened: Thursday November 17th 1983 at 8.30pm.

Episode 3: Friday The 14th
The Trotters are bound for Cornwall and a weekends fishing. It should be a relaxing break… if they can forget about the roaming escaped murderer who might be closer than they think.

First screened: Thursday November 24th 1983 at 8.30pm.

The Official Only Fools and Horses Quiz Book

Episode 4: Yesterday Never Comes
Del's into art dealing in a big way, especially since meeting the glamorous antiques dealer, Miranda. But has she really fallen for his charms or are her motives more mercenary?

First screened: Thursday December 1st 1983 at 8.30pm.

Episode 5: May The Force Be With You
Del's old nemesis, Roy Slater, is back in town, hell bent on revenge and brandishing a new police warrant card. When the Trotters end up in the nick, Del comes up with a plan to set them free.

First screened: Thursday December 8th 1983 at 8.30pm.

☆ ☆ ☆

Episode 6: Wanted
Rodney? London's most wanted criminal? Surely there must be a mistake! Actually it's just Del winding him up. But that doesn't stop him going on the run.

First screened: Thursday December 15th 1983 at 8.30pm.

☆ ☆ ☆

Episode 7: Who's A Pretty Boy?
When Denzil and his wife need their flat re-decorated, Del convinces him that the Trotters are the men for the job. But nobody said anything about a dead canary in the kitchen.

First screened: Thursday December 22nd 1983 at 8.30pm.

Episode 8: Thicker Than Water
The Trotter's Christmas is ruined when Del and Rodney's long lost father, Reg, comes back into their lives, especially when he starts casting doubts on Del's true parentage.

First screened: Sunday December 25th 1983 at 9.35pm.

☆ ☆ QUIZ THREE – SERIES THREE

1. In *Homesick* what is the name of the cigarette puffing chairman of the town hall's tenants association?

....

2. Who is voted in as the new vice chairman?

....

3. In *Friday The 14th* the Trotters go away for a weekend's fishing. Whose holiday cottage do they stay in?

....

4. What particular fish are they looking to catch?

....

5. In which Cornish village is the cottage?

....

6. In *May The Force Be With You* who does Del claim once put itching powder in Slater's belly button?

....

7. In *Yesterday Never Comes* what is the surname of Miranda, the antiques dealer who cons Del in order to get her hands on his gran's painting?

....

48

QUIZ THREE – SERIES THREE

8. In which part of London is Miranda's shop?

....

9. What is the name of the furniture restorer who works at Miranda's shop?

....

10. In *Healthy Competition* what kind of 'agricultural machinery' does Rodney buy at auction, despite Del's warning not to?

....

11. Who was selling the machinery at the auction?

....

12. Who was originally selling the machinery?

a) Harry Dando
b) Old man Corby
c) Alfie Flowers ....

13. In *Wanted* what popular 80s song is Rodney singing as he walks home from the pub?

....

14. In the opening scene of *Thicker Than Water* Del is out with a new girlfriend. What famous dog does Rodney refer to her as?

a) Rin Tin Tin **b)** Snowy **c)** Lassie ....

15. In *Thicker Than Water* what letter is added to Del's blood test result?

a) 'b' **b)** 'o' **c)** 'a'...

16. In *Homesick* what is the name of the doctor who examines Grandad?

....

17. The doctor likens Grandad's legs to which famous racehorse?

a) Arkle **b)** Nijinsky **c)** Red Rum.................................

18. In *Healthy Competition* who does Rodney go into a brief business partnership with?

....

19. In *May The Force Be With You* Trigger claims he once owned a hat. What colour was it?

....

20. Thanks to Del, what kind of cake did Denzil and his wife end up cutting on their wedding day?

a) Eccles cake
b) Jam sponge
c) Bakewell tart ....

21. In *Friday The 14th* what does a sore losing Rodney refer to as a "stupid bloody game"?

....

22. In *Homesick* what is Del selling at the market?

....

23. In *Thicker Than Water* Del and Rodney's estranged dad, Reg, comes back into their lives. To make up for all the lost years where does Reg take Rodney for a day out?

....

24. Whose bedroom does Reg take?

....

25. In *Friday The 14th* what is the escaped murderer's weapon of choice?

....

26. In *May The Force Be With You* Slater asks Trigger if he is still doing a 'double act' with?

a) Paddy The Greek
b) Monkey Harris
c) Tommy Razzle ....

27. In *Healthy Competition* which member of the Royal family does Del claim owns one of the toy puppies he is selling?

....

28. According to Del, where were the toy puppies made?

a) Hong Kong
b) Taiwan
c) Burma ....

29. In *Who's A Pretty Boy?* what is the name of the pet store where Grandad buys an emergency canary?

....

30. What is the store owner's first name?

....

31. What is the name of the store owner's 'treasured' pet canary?

....

32. How much money does Grandad pay for the new canary?

....

33. How much money does he tell Del he paid for it?

....

34. In *Healthy Competition* where does Mickey Pearce go on holiday?

....

35. In *Homesick* which TV show was Grandad just about to switch over to when he 'collapsed'?

a) Coronation Street
b) Dallas
c) Crossroads ....

36. In *Yesterday Never Comes* Del advertises his 'antique' cabinet as dating back to which monarch?

....

37. According to Miranda, under the reign of which monarch was the cabinet actually made?

....

53

The Official Only Fools and Horses Quiz Book

38. In *May The Force Be With You* what TV show does Grandad try to tune into a microwave oven?

....

39. In *Homesick* what is Rodney disappointed to discover Grandad has got him for dinner?

....

40. In *Wanted* what is the name of the hysterical woman who accuses Rodney of assault?

....

41. In an attempt to calm her down what does Rodney claim to be?

a) A doctor
b) A priest
c) A policeman ....

42. In *Thicker Than Water* what does Reg write on the back of one Rodney's GCE certificates?

....

43. In *Homesick* what fruit does Rodney buy for Grandad that Del puts with 'the other three thousand?

a) Grapes   **b)** Oranges   **c)** Pineapples ....

44. In *May The Force Be With You* what rank is Roy Slater in the police force?

....

45. Which part of London was Slater stationed in before being transferred back to Peckham?

a) North **b)** East **c)** West ....

46. In *Healthy Competition* what is the name of the Indian restaurant that Del has a meal in?

....

47. In *Homesick* Del mentions a local lady who reported being indecently assaulted after a punter's cheque bounced. What is her full name?

....

48. In *Yesterday Never Comes* what third rate type of meal does Del 'treat' Miranda to?

a) Fish and Chips
b) Curry
c) Chinese ....

49. The morning after his meal with Miranda what does Del complain he has a touch of?

....

50. At which famous battle does Grandad claim his grandad was killed?

....

51. According to Grandad, what did his grandad have in his breast pocket that 'saved' him from a sniper's bullet?

....

52. When he and his school mates used to play pirates, which pirate would Del play?

a) Blue Beard
b) Long John Silver
c) Dan Tempest ....

53. Which roll did Slater always play?

....

54. In *Friday The 14th* what is the name of the fish restaurant where Del says he had a meeting with Boycie?

....

55. In *May The Force Be With You* who stole the microwave?

....

56. In *Wanted* what does Del claim the police have nicknamed Rodney?

....

57. In *Homesick* by which name does Miss McKenzie insist Del call her?

....

58. What does Miss McKenzie claim she wanted to be when she left school?

....

59. In *Friday The 14th* what is the full name of the gamekeeper?

....

60. What medical condition does he suffer with?

....

61. In *Thicker Than Water* Reg Trotter claims that he has been staying at an infirmary in which northern city?

a) Newcastle
b) Leeds
c) Sheffield ....

62. In *Healthy Competition* which of Del's associates does he enlist the help of in order to reform his partnership with Rodney?

....

63. In *Who's A Pretty Boy?* Del uses Denzil's phone to call an old acquaintance who has emigrated. What is his name?

....

64. Where has he emigrated to?

a) America
b) Canada
c) Australia ....

65. In *Friday The 14th* what is the name of the Chief of Security at the mental institution?

....

66. In *Wanted* what does Rodney forget to take with him when he goes 'on the run'?

....

67. In *Wanted* what type of room is Rodney found hiding in?

....

68. Rodney's hiding place is given away by the smell of what wafting through the flats?

....

69. In *Yesterday Never Comes* what does Rodney receive in return for smacking a woman's bum?

....

70. In *Who's A Pretty Boy?* what is the surname of Brendan, the Irish painter and decorator Del and Rodney meet in the Nag's Head?

....

71. Brendan recently sold Del some paint. What colour was it?

....

72. In *Yesterday Never Comes* Del surprises Miranda by making her a drink called a 'Tequila Sunset'. What spirit does Del use instead of Tequila?

....

73. What is the nationality of the Trotter's upstairs neighbour who gave Del the recipe for the drink?

....

74. In *Friday The 14th* what game does Del play an imaginary version of?

....

75. In *Who's A Pretty Boy?* what is the name of the canary the Trotter's believe they have killed?

....

76. In *Friday The 14th* the escaped murderer panics when he hears a helicopter overhead. Del calms him by telling him it is…?

....

77. In *Yesterday Never Comes* what is the name of the auction house where Miranda sells Del's gran's painting?

....

78. How did Del's gran come to acquire the painting?

....

79. What was the name of the painting's artist?

....

80. In *Yesterday Never Comes* what LP of Del's does he offer to put on for Miranda?

a) His Bobby Crush LP
b) His Johnny Cash Live At San Quentin LP
c) His Richard Clayderman LP ....

81. In *Wanted* what are Del, Boycie and Trigger doing in the Nag's Head that an overhead sign forbids?

....

82. In *Who's A Pretty Boy?* what is the name of the Nag's Head barmaid whose dad has bought a camel hair coat off Del?

....

83. In *Wanted* what local take-away has been destroyed by fire?

a) The curry house
b) The burger bar
c) The kebab house ....

84. In *Healthy Competition* what does Del tell Grandad he wouldn't like up his nose as a wart?

....

85. In *Who's A Pretty Boy?* Mike takes over as the new landlord of the Nag's Head. What is his surname?

....

SERIES
★ ★ ★ ★ ★ ★ ★ ★
FOUR

SERIES FOUR EPISODE GUIDE

Episode 1: Happy Returns
Rodney has found the first girlfriend who has ever really meant something to him. The trouble is, she might be his niece.

First screened: Thursday February 21st 1985 at 8.00pm.

Episode 2: Strained Relations
Grandad's funeral brings the relations out of the wood work – including the Trotter boys' uncle Albert. Now it's just a tricky case of how to get rid of him.

First screened: Thursday February 28th 1985 at 8.00pm.

Episode 3: Hole In One
Thanks to Rodney's business acumen the Trotters are completely skint. Time for Uncle Albert to display his uncanny talent for falling down holes without hurting himself.

First screened: Thursday March 7th 1985 at 8.00pm.

Episode 4: It's Only Rock And Roll
When Rodney joins an up and coming pop group, Del spots an opportunity for a quick earner.

First screened: Thursday March 14th 1985 at 8.00pm.

Episode 5: Sleeping Dogs Lie
Looking after Boycie and Marlene's new puppy while they're on holiday should be a doddle, but after one night in the flat, the Trotter curse strikes again and the dog becomes comatose. Or is there a more simple explanation?

First screened: Thursday March 21st 1985 at 8.00pm.

Episode 6: Watching The Girls Go By
Rodney is desperate to find a date for the Nag's Head party and win a bet with Mickey Pearce. With Del's help it should be plain sailing.

First screened: Thursday March 28th 1985 at 8.00pm.

Episode 7: As One Door Closes
When the bottom falls out of a lucrative business deal, times get hard for the Trotters. But nature will find a way as Del and Rodders go butterfly collecting…

First screened: Thursday April 4th 1985 at 8.00pm.

QUIZ FOUR – SERIES FOUR

1. In *Happy Returns* what type of shop does Rodney's new girlfriend, Debbie, work in?

a) Laundrette **b)** Newsagents **c)** Fishmongers ....

2. In *Watching The Girls Go By* what do Del and Rodney convince Albert is in the hood of his duffel coat?

....

3. In *It's Only Rock and Roll* Rodney claims his new band are styling themselves on which chart topping pop group?

a) Spandau Ballet
b) Duran Duran
c) Frankie Goes To Hollywood ....

4. In *Strained Relations* who does Del claim to have more bounce than?

....

5. In *As One Door Closes* what kind of DIY kit is Del trying to sell at the market?

....

6. In *Sleeping Dogs Lie* Boycie has bought Marlene a new 'puppy'. What breed of dog is it?

a) Rottweiler **b)** Doberman **c)** Great Dane ....

38. In *The Class Of '62* how many people, including Slater, attend the school reunion?

....

39. In *He Ain't Heavy, He's My Uncle* how many muggers does Uncle Albert originally claim attacked him?

....

40. In *The Sky's The Limit* what country have Cassandra and her mum gone on holiday to?

a) Spain **b)** Italy **c)** Portugal ....

41. In *Three Men, A Woman and A Baby* what does Rodney wear in an attempt to impress Cassandra?

....

42. What does Cassandra later mistake it for?

....

43. In *The Class Of '62* who does Trigger suggest might have organised the surprise school reunion?

....

32. In *The Class Of '62* Slater claims that he has been living in what Essex town?

....

33. In *The Sky's The Limit*, what, according to Boycie, is the profession of his next door neighbour?

....

34. In *The Chance Of A Lunchtime* Rodney resigns from his job. What is the name of the assistant who replaces him?

....

35. In *Stage Fright* the council Housing Department offers Rodney a LDA. What does Rodney hope LDA stands for?

....

36. What does he later discover LDA actually stands for?

....

37. In *The Sky's The Limit* Rodney gets Albert to phone in sick for him. What 'medical condition' does Albert say Rodney is suffering with?

....

26. What number is on the door?

a) 2
b) 12
c) 21 ....

27. In *The Sky's The Limit* what has Mike banned Albert from doing in the Nag's Head?

....

28. In *He Ain't Heavy, He's My Uncle* Rodney tells Cassandra the suit he is wearing was made where?

....

29. In *Three Men, A Woman and A Baby* what, according to Trigger, does Del want to name his and Raquel's baby if it's a girl?

....

30. What, according to Albert, are they thinking of calling it if it's a boy?

....

31. In *The Sky's The Limit* what is the name of the hotel Del desperately tries to recall?

....

21. In *The Class Of '62* which famous author does Trigger claim to have once fancied?

....

22. In *He Ain't Heavy, He's My Uncle* what is the nickname of Uncle Albert's rival dominoes player?

....

23. In *The Sky's The Limit* Del claims that going for a drink with Cassandra's dad is like going on a pub crawl with who?

....

24. In *The Class of '62* Del receives his first ever fax message. Who is it from?

a) Boycie
b) Ronnie Nelson
c) Mike ....

25. In *The Chance Of A Lunchtime* what country's national anthem plays when Rodney rings the doorbell at his and Cassandra's flat?

a) France
b) Germany
c) America ....

7. What is the dog's name?

....

8. According to Del how much money did Boycie pay for the dog?

a) £400   **b)** £500   **c)** £600 ....

9. In *Hole In One* what is the full name of the dodgy solicitor Del hires to sue the brewery?

....

10. Del and Albie Littlewood once let down the tyres of which type of vehicle?

a) Bus   **b)** Milk float   **c)** Police car ....

11. In *It's Only Rock and Roll* what is band leader, Mental Mickey's, surname?

....

12. Which psychiatric hospital does Mental Mickey deny ever being treated in?

....

13. In *As One Door Closes* what does Del desperately need two grand to buy?

....

67

14. In *Strained Relations* what does Del cook that Rodney refuses to eat because "it tastes nice"?

....

15. In *As One Door Closes* what is the common name of the rare butterfly in Rodney's magazine?

....

16. According to the magazine which London park has the butterfly been spotted in?

....

17. How much reward money is being offered for its safe capture?

....

18. In the opening scene of *Happy Returns* what does Rodney ask Del to buy him?

....

19. In *Hole In One* it is revealed in court that Uncle Albert spent the best part of the war stationed at a storage depot in The Isle of...?

a) Man   **b)** Wight   **c)** Dogs ....

20. In *Sleeping Dogs Lie* where are Boycie and Marlene going on holiday?

a) Mauritius
b) The Seychelles
c) The Maldives ....

21. In *Strained Relations* whose hat does Del mistake for Grandad's?

....

22. In *Happy Returns* what is the name of June's mischievous son?

a) Jason **b)** Darren **c)** Wayne ....

23. In *As One Door Closes* who very reluctantly lends Del their redundancy money?

....

24. In *Strained Relations* what, according to Uncle Albert, was his nickname in the navy?

....

25. In *It's Only Rock and Roll* what instrument does Rodney play in his new band?

....

26. In *Hole In One* what has Rodney spent the last of the firm's money on, despite it being the worst winter in two million years?

....

27. According to Del's old flame, June, what year did she and Del split up?

....

28. What is the name of the flats where June lives?

a) Desmond Tutu House
b) Nelson Mandela House
c) Zimbabwe House   ....

29. In *Sleeping Dogs Lie* what type of food poisoning is Uncle Albert suspected of having?

a) E. Coli   **b)** Botulism   **c)** Salmonella   ....

30. In *Hole In One* Del claims that Uncle Albert has been down more holes than...?

....

31. In *Watching The Girls Go By* Albert reminisces about a German woman he fell in love with. What was her name?

....

70

32. In what city did they meet?

a) Munich **b)** Frankfurt **c)** Hamburg ....

33. According to Albert, how many fingers did she have?

....

34. Rodney's band appear on Top of The Pops going by what name?

....

35. What is the name of the song with which they make it into the charts?

....

36. What position are they in the charts?

....

37. What was Albie Littlewood taking a shortcut across when he was killed?

....

38. What was the name of Albie Littlewood's girlfriend at the time of his death?

....

39. In *As One Door Closes* where does Albert claim he was in 1959?

a) Calcutta **b)** Delhi **c)** Bombay ....

40. In *Strained Relations* what does Mike claim was stolen from the Nag's Head along with a sonic burglar alarm?

....

41. Who sold Mike the sonic burglar alarm?

....

42. In the opening scene of *Watching The Girls Go By* what song is Uncle Albert playing on the Nag's Head piano?

....

43. In *Sleeping Dogs Lie* how many days have the Trotters been looking after the dog before it becomes 'ill'?

a) 1 day **b)** 2 days **c)** 3 days ....

44. What nickname was given to Albert by insurance companies?

....

45. In *Happy Returns* where does June say her absent husband is working?

....

46. She later admits that he is actually in prison for stealing what?

....

47. In *Watching The Girls Go By* Rodney and Mickey Pearce have a bet for how much money?

....

48. In *Happy Returns* what marshal art does Mickey Pearce claim to be learning at evening school?

a) Tae Kwon Do **b)** Kung Fu **c)** Aikido ....

49. What is the name of the club in Deptford where Rodney's band plays its first gig?

....

50. What is the club owner's name?

....

51. What is the name of the club's banged up resident band?

....

52. In *Strained Relations* how many times does Uncle Albert claim he has been torpedoed?

a) 3 times **b)** 4 times **c)** 5 times ....

53. In *Happy Returns* Rodney brings the empty record sleeve of which band to his date with Debbie?

a) Tears For Fears
b) Spandau Ballet
c) Duran Duran ....

54. In *Watching The Girls Go By* who does Rodney claim he bought his new and very striking suit from?

....

55. Where does Del confess to being on the night Albie Littlewood died?

....

56. In *Strained Relations* what is the name of the couple Albert has been living with?

a) John and Eileen
b) Dave and Sue
c) Stan and Jean ....

70. In *Hole In One* Del mentions that he has ordered Grandad's headstone. What bird of prey does he say is featured on it?

a) Falcon **b)** Eagle **c)** Hawk ....

71. In *Hole In One*, as well as the use of his legs, what else does Albert pretend to have lost?

....

72. In *Happy Returns* who does June's son mistake for the Bogeyman?

....

73. In *Happy Returns* what LP does Del offer to pop home and get for June?

....

74. In *Sleeping Dogs Lie*, who, according to Rodney, has "been on the Bob Martins"?

....

75. In *As One Door Closes* at what location do the Trotters first spot the butterfly?

....

★ ★ ★

SERIES FIVE EPISODE GUIDE

Episode 1: From Prussia With Love
When a foreign damsel in distress turns up in the Nag's Head, the Trotters sweep in to save her. The trouble is she's 8 months pregnant. Still, Del's got an idea…

First screened: Sunday August 31st 1986 at 8.35pm.

Episode 2: The Miracle Of Peckham
When Del goes to church to confess, he ends up witnessing a miracle. Has he caught religion or is he just pulling a fast one?

First screened: Sunday September 7th 1986 at 8.35pm.

Episode 3: The Longest Night
The Trotters get their weekly shopping in at the local supermarket and end up being held hostage at gun-point for the night.

First screened: Sunday September 14th 1986 at 8.35pm.

Episode 4: Tea For Three
When the Trotter brothers compete for a girl's affection, Del sees to it that Rodney ends up with a red face – literally. Still, revenge should be particularly sweet when Rodney volunteers Del for a spot of hang-gliding.

First screened: Sunday September 22nd 1986 at 8.35pm.

The Official Only Fools and Horses Quiz Book

Episode 5: Video Nasty
When Rodney is given a grant to make a local community film, Del immediately spots the earning potential. Meanwhile Mickey Pearce is busy making an entirely different type of film.

First screened: Sunday September 28th 1986 at 8.35pm.

Episode 6: Who Wants To Be A Millionaire?
When Del's old business partner, Jumbo, shows up back in Peckham with tales of his booming overseas business, the Trotters end up on the verge of emigrating. That is until Rodney's emigration visa is turned down. Could Del really leave Peckham and his family behind?

First screened: Sunday October 5th 1986 at 8.35pm.

QUIZ FIVE - SERIES FIVE

1. In *From Prussia With Love* what nationality is Anna, the stranded and very pregnant girl who stays with the Trotters?

....

2. What nationality had Rodney hoped she was?

....

3. In *Tea For Three* where was the television transmitter that Del crashed into?

....

4. In *Video Nasty* Rodney has been given the task of writing a local community film for his art class. Who is directing the film?

....

5. What is the name of the supermarket where the Trotters spend *The Longest Night*?

....

6. How much is the supermarket offering its millionth customer?

a) £500   b) £1,000   c) £2,000   ....

7. What shop does Del suggest the Trotters do their shopping at in future?

....

8. In *Tea For Three* who wins the Nag's Head Talent Contest?

....

9. In *From Prussia With Love* who does Boycie and Marlene's dog take a particular liking to in their back garden?

....

10. In *Video Nasty* Boycie has started up a pirate video business. Who has he employed to deliver the videos?

....

11. In *Who Wants To Be A Millionaire?* Jumbo wants Del to be a partner in his new business importing what?

....

12. In *The Longest Night* how many hours are the Trotters held hostage for?

a) 10 hours **b)** 12 hours **c)** 14 hours ....

13. In *Who Wants To Be A Millionaire?* what job has Del got planned for Rodney when they emigrate?

....

14. In *From Prussia With Love* what restaurant does Rodney take Anna to before they go back to Nelson Mandela House?

a) The Star Of Bengal
b) The Golden Lotus
c) The Light Of Nepal ....

15. What county are the Trotters in when Del goes hang gliding?

a) Berkshire **b)** Sussex **c)** Hampshire ....

16. In *The Miracle Of Peckham* what cassette does Rodney worriedly discover is missing from Del's collection?

a) His Johnny Cash cassette
b) His Bobby Crush cassette
c) His Cliff Richard cassette ....

17. In *The Longest Night* Del claims he has a date planned with the croupier of which club?

....

18. In *Tea For Three* Del and Rodney receive the news that their aunt has been rushed to hospital. What is her name?

....

19. In *Video Nasty* what is the name of the adult film Mickey Pearce shoots in the Trotter's flat?

....

20. In *The Miracle of Peckham* what is the name of the dilapidated hospice that is going to be demolished?

a) St Mary's **b)** St Anne's **c)** St Catherine's ....

21. What charity event does Del suggest holding to help save the hospice?

....

22. How much money needs to be raised in order to save the hospice?

a) £85,000 **b)** £118,000 **c)** £185,000 ....

23. Which page 3 model does Del suggest re-open the hospice?

a) Linda Lusardi
b) Maria Whittaker
c) Samantha Fox ....

24. In *From Prussia With Love* what does Anna say she does for a job?

....

25. In *Video Nasty* what is the title of Del's film idea?

....

26. In *The Longest Night* what is the full name of the supermarket's head of security?

....

27. The head of security claims he once served in which African country's police force?

a) Nigeria   **b)** Zimbabwe   **c)** Kenya ....

28. In *Who Wants To Be A Millionaire?* what, according to Jumbo, has caused his 'temporary' baldness?

....

29. In *Tea For Three* who brings the 'paralysed' Del back from hospital?

a) Trigger and Denzil
b) Trigger and Mike
c) Trigger and Boycie ....

The Official Only Fools and Horses Quiz Book

30. In *The Miracle Of Peckham* what kind of musical instrument does Rodney 'borrow' from Biffo the bear?

a) Saxophone **b)** Banjo **c)** Trumpet ....

31. In *Tea For Three* Del claims that he did a loop-the-loop over which town?

....

32. In *From Prussia With Love* which famous sports star does Del Boy say is Anna's cousin?

....

33. In *The Miracle Of Peckham* what is the name of the woman Rodney says he met in the Nag's Head, who apparently has the hots for him?

....

34. Rodney likens her to which cast member of the TV show Dynasty?

a) Joan Collins
b) Linda Evans
c) George Hamilton ....

35. According to Del, how tall is this woman?

a) 4ft 10 **b)** 5ft 5 **c)** 6ft 6 ....

36. In *Tea For Three* what does Del try to sell Mike in the Nag's Head?

....

37. In *The Longest Night* Rodney is on edge because he is trying to give up...?

a) Smoking
b) Drinking
c) Adult art magazines ....

38. In *Video Nasty* what is the name of Mickey Pearce's punk rocker girlfriend?

....

39. What is Del's ex business partner, Jumbo's, surname?

....

40. Where did Jumbo emigrate to?

a) America b) Australia c) Canada ....

41. According to Del what kind of stall did he and Jumbo used to run?

a) A fish stall
b) A fruit and veg stall
c) A flower stall ....

42. In *From Prussia With Love* what is the brand name of the cordless telephones Del is trying to sell?

....

43. In *The Longest Night* how much does the Trotter's shopping cost?

a) £32.90 **b)** £29.48 **c)** £26.42 ....

44. In *The Miracle Of Peckham* what make of aftershave does Rodney sprinkle all over Albert's breakfast?

a) Old Spice **b)** Hai Karate **c)** Brut ....

45. What is Albert having for breakfast?

a) Haddock **b)** Trout **c)** Kipper ....

46. In *Tea For Three* what does Rodney contribute to his, Del's and Lisa's tea?

....

47. In *From Prussia With Love* what is the full name of Anna's baby's father?

....

48. Which advertising slogan does Del use to comfort Anna when her labour contractions start?

....

49. In *The Miracle of Peckham* what does Del buy that leads him to confess in church?

....

50. What two "honest and upstanding gentlemen" does Del confess to buying the hooky gear from?

a) Towser and Ugandan Morris
b) Sunglasses Ron and Paddy the Greek
c) Trigger and Monkey Harris ....

51. In *Video Nasty* which two 'businessmen' are backing Boycie in his pirate video venture?

....

52. In *From Prussia With Love* what name do Boycie and Marlene plan to give their new adopted son?

a) Derek **b)** Mark **c)** Tyler.......................................

53. In *Video Nasty* Del buys Rodney a typewriter. Which Monarch's crest is on it?

....

54. Which two letters on the typewriter are missing?

a) The E and O
b) The A and S
c) The T and A ....

55. In *The Longest Night* what is the name of the supermarket's manager?

a) Mr Wilkinson
b) Mr Henderson
c) Mr Peterson ....

56. What is the supermarket manager's wife cooking him for dinner?

a) Boeuf Bourguignon
b) Coq au Vin
c) Entrecote Rioja ....

57. What is his wife's name?

a) Marjory **b)** Deidre **c)** Valerie ....

58. In *From Prussia With Love* what sex is Anna's baby?

....

59. At the end of *The Miracle Of Peckham* who chases Rodney down the street?

....

60. In *Tea For Three* what relation is Lisa to Trigger?

....

61. What town does Lisa say she is living just outside of?

....

62. How old is Lisa?

a) 25 **b)** 30 **c)** 35 ....

63. What nickname did Del give Lisa's mum?

a) Miss 999
b) The Rose Of Peckham
c) The Bull Dog ....

64. What is the name of Lisa's high flying fiancé?

a) Steven **b)** Paul **c)** Andy ....

65. In *The Longest Night* how much money is claimed to be in the manager's office safe?

a) £60,000 **b)** £85,000 **c)** £100,000 ....

66. In *Tea For Three* Rodney tells Lisa that Del is about to celebrate which birthday?

a) 44th **b)** 45th **c)** 46th ....

67. In *The Longest Night* what type of 'gun' does the armed robber use?

a) A Smith and Wesson
b) A Luger
c) A Beretta ....

68. Where does the head of security confess the gun came from?

....

69. In *Video Nasty* which wedding anniversary are Boycie and Marlene celebrating?

a) 15th
b) 20th
c) 25th ....

70. In *The Longest Night* what does the armed robber claim the police have nicknamed him?

a) The Phantom
b) The Panther
c) The Shadow ....

71. After recognising Del, who does the armed robber reveal himself to be? (Full name)

....

72. In *Tea For Three* what type of soldier does Del tell Lisa he used to be?

....

73. In *Video Nasty* the head of Rodney's art group is a Mr...?

a) Simons
b) Stuart
c) Stevens ....

74. In *Video Nasty* what is the name of the local sauna parlour Del suggests Rodney mention in his film script?

....

75. In the opening scene of *Who Wants To Be A Millionaire?*, Del interrupts a business meeting in the Nag's Head between Jumbo and who?

....

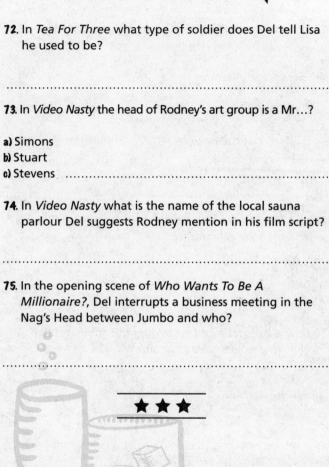

SERIES
★★★★★★★★★★
SIX

SERIES SIX EPISODE GUIDE

Episode 1: Yuppy Love
Del enters the exciting world of red braces, filofaxes and yuppy sorts. Meanwhile Rodney's on the pull with classy new girlfriend, Cassandra. But what will she think of Nelson Mandela House?

First screened: Sunday January 8th 1989 at 7.15pm.

Episode 2: Danger UXD
When Del takes possession of a consignment of dolls for absolutely nothing, he's well pleased. But on taking the dolls out of their boxes it quickly becomes clear that he won't be selling them down the market.

First screened: Sunday January 15th 1989 at 7.15pm.

Episode 3: Chain Gang
Faced with the opportunity to buy a batch of gold chains off new associate, Arnie, Del can't resist and puts together a consortium to raise the money. But when Arnie is taken seriously ill just as the deal is about to be clinched, Del can't help but feel that all that glitters…

First screened: Sunday January 22nd 1989 at 7.15pm.

The Official Only Fools and Horses Quiz Book

Episode 4: The Unlucky Winner Is ......

When Rodney wins a holiday for three in a competition that he never even entered, he can't wait to get to the hotel, crack open the duty free drink and spend some quality time with Cassandra. The only snag is he's got to pretend to be a teenager for the entire duration of the holiday.

First screened: Sunday January 29th 1989 at 7.15pm.

Episode 5: Sickness And Wealth

When a suffering Del reluctantly visits the doctor he is admitted to hospital. Del worries it could be something fatal. Or could it just be that the cigars, booze and curries are finally catching up with him?

First screened: Sunday February 5th 1989 at 7.15pm.

Episode 6: Little Problems

As a wedding present for Rodney and Cassandra, Del promises to take care of Rodney's share of his deposit for a new flat. That is if the Driscoll brothers don't take care of him first.

First screened: Sunday February 12th 1989 at 7.15pm.

QUIZ SIX - SERIES SIX

1. In *Yuppy Love* what character in the film *Wall Street* is Del styling himself on?

....

2. What is the name of the casino in the opening scene of *Chain Gang*?

....

3. What is the name of the casino's doorman?

....

4. In *Little Problems* how much money does Del owe the Driscoll brothers?

a) £1,000 **b)** £2,000 **c)** £3,000 ....

5. In *The Unlucky Winner Is...* what is the title of Rodney's prize winning painting?

....

6. What famous monument had Rodney originally intended to paint?

....

7. Where does the painting win a holiday to?

a) Mallorca
b) Lanzarote
c) Menorca ....

8. In *Danger UXD* what is the Trotter's fridge full up with?

....

9. In *Sickness and Wealth* which room in the Trotter's flat does Elsie Partridge suspect is haunted?

....

10. What was the name of the estate Del once sent Rodney to with a barrow load of gas conversion kits?

....

11. In *Danger UXD* which 80s pop duet does Del refer to the blow up dolls as?

....

12. In *Chain Gang* Cassandra goes on a week's training course where?

....

13. What is the name of the hotel where Cassandra attends the course?

....

14. Who of the following was **not** in Elsie Partridge's séance at the Nag's Head?

a) Mike
b) Denzil
c) Trigger ....

15. How many people, including Elsie, participate in the séance?

....

16. Which deceased relative of Boycie's makes contact at the séance?

....

17. When Del and Rodney's mum makes 'contact', who does Trigger mistake her for?

....

18. Who walks in on the séance, bringing it to an abrupt end?

....

19. In *The Unlucky Winner Is...* how old does Rodney pretend to be?

a) 13
b) 14
c) 15 ....

20. In *Little Problems* what gets briefly stuck up Del's nose?

....

21. In *Yuppy Love* Trigger claims he has been barred from the Nag's Head for stealing what?

....

22. In Danger UXD how many blow-up dolls do Del and Rodney take off Denzil's hands?

....

23. In *Danger UXD* who does Del try to sell the dolls to?

....

24. In *Sickness and Wealth* Uncle Albert claims that he bought what off the bloke upstairs?

....

25. In *Danger UXD* what are the names of the two dolls that self inflate in the Trotter's flat?

a) Saucy Susan and Juicy Lucy
b) Lusty Linda and Erotic Estelle
c) Randy Mandy and Busty Barbara ....

26. In *Little Problems* what nationality is the kid who attempts to fix Del's dodgy video recorders?

....

27. Where on the estate does the kid live?

a) Nelson Mandela House
b) Zimbabwe House
c) Desmond Tutu House ....

28. In *Little Problems* what type of sign does Rodney have stuck to his crotch on his stag night?

....

29. In *Danger UXD* the blow-up dolls have been accidentally filled with which explosive gas?

a) Methane
b) Propane
c) Butane ....

101

30. In *Yuppy Love* which infamous assassin does Albert say Del bears a resemblance to?

....

31. In *The Unlucky Winner Is...* what is the full name of the male tour rep?

....

32. What is the name of the female tour rep?

....

33. In *Danger UXD* what is the name of the company Denzil collected the dolls from?

....

34. In *Yuppy Love* Del attempts to impress two yuppy women by telling them he has just bought shares in which 'little' department store?

....

35. In *Sickness and Wealth* what does Del stir Andrews Liver Salts into, to help his stomach pains?

....

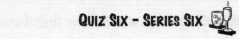

36. What is the name of Denzil's new haulage company?

....

37. In *Chain Gang* what does Boycie pretend to be which ends up seeing him getting punched on the nose?

....

38. In *Yuppy Love* Rodney is studying for a diploma in what?

....

39. In *Little Problems* what is Rodney's middle name revealed to be?

....

40. In *The Unlucky Winner Is...* Rodney takes part in a Skateboard Derby. What position does he finish?

a) 1st
b) 2nd
c) 3rd ....

41. According to Rodney what caused him to fall off his skateboard?

....

42. In *Chain Gang* Del creates a consortium to raise the money to buy the gold chains. How many people make up the consortium?

....

43. Who of the following is **not** part of the consortium?

a) Denzil
b) Albert
c) Mike ....

44. Whose aunty had to pawn their necklace in order to help raise his consortium money?

....

45. How much does Rodney contribute to the consortium money?

a) £36.24
b) £37.63
o) £38.42 ....

46. In *Chain Gang* how many chains do Del and his consortium buy off Arnie?

a) 150
b) 200
c) 250 ....

47. In *Yuppy Love* which bottle of wine does Del order in the yuppy wine bar?

....

48. In *Sickness and Wealth* what is the full name of the Scottish doctor who is put in charge of Del's case?

....

49. What does he diagnose Del with?

....

50. In *Danger UXD* Mike charges Denzil £1 for a bowl of stew. How much does he charge a yuppy for his bowl of 'boeuf bourguignon'?

....

51. In *Danger UXD* Del is selling video recorders. Where were they made?

....

52. In *Yuppy Love* what song do Rodney and Cassandra dance to?

....

53. In *The Unlucky Winner Is...* what is the full name of Uncle Albert's date?

....

54. In *Danger UXD* what is the name of the Chinese take-away where Denzil discovers the truth about the blow-up dolls?

a) Golden Dragon
b) China Gardens
c) Golden Lotus ....

55. In *Yuppy Love* in what part of London does Cassandra say she lives?

....

56. What initials follow Rodney's name on the Trotters Independent Traders personalised note paper?

....

57. In *Yuppy Love* Rodney claims Mickey Pearce took his last girlfriend to a concert by which pop group?

....

58. In *Yuppy Love* Mickey Pearce claims that Del's new green coat makes him look like whose little boy?

....

59. In *Danger UXD* Del had a date planned with a woman from the cut price butchers. What is her name?

....

60. According to Del, what had she promised him?

....

61. In *Chain Gang* what is the full name of the business man Arnie arranges to meet for lunch?

....

62. In *Little Problems* what is the name of the evening school teacher who Del pays to re-mark Rodney's diploma?

....

63. In *The Unlucky Winner Is...* what gang does Rodney reluctantly become a lifelong member of?

....

64. In the opening scene of *Danger UXD* who does Rodney say he and Cassandra went to see play at the Royal Albert Hall?

a) Eric Clapton
b) Wet Wet Wet
c) Fergal Sharkey ....

65. In *Sickness and Wealth* what shocking news does Marlene receive?

....

66. In *Chain Gang* Arnie claims that he is a retired what?

....

67. In *Chain Gang* what does Arnie claim his wife's name is?

....

68. According to Arnie, what are his two sons called?

a) Lee and Darren
b) Daniel and James
c) Steven and Gary ....

69. In *Yuppy Love* who first asks Cassandra for a dance?

....

70. In *Sickness and Wealth* what kind of sandwich does Rodney smuggle into hospital for Del?

....

71. According to Del, what tourist attraction was he working at when he met a Texan oil baron's daughter?

....

72. In *Sickness and Wealth* which illness does Albert speculate Del might be suffering with?

....

73. In *Yuppy Love* Rodney claims Del is selling raincoats with what written on the label?

....

74. In *The Unlucky Winner Is...* what is the name of Rodney's 13-year-old admirer?

....

75. Which 80s boy band is she a fan of?

....

76. In *Little Problems* who has Del bought 100 executive mobile phones from?

a) Trigger and Monkey Harris
b) Mickey Pearce and Jevon
c) Sunglasses Ron and Paddy the Greek ....

77. In *Yuppy Love* what is the name of the road Rodney pretends he lives in?

....

78. In *Sickness and Wealth* what is revealed to be Boycie's middle name?

....

79. In *Yuppy Love* which band, according to Del, can you not 'whack'?

a) The Who
b) Status Quo
c) The Kinks ....

80. In *Little Problems* who offers Rodney a new job?

....

81. In *The Unlucky Winner Is...* what relation of Rodney's does Cassandra pretend to be?

....

82. In *Yuppy Love* what is Cassandra's friend's name?

....

83. At the end of *Sickness and Wealth* what shocking news does Rodney break to Del?

....

84. In *Little Problems* Rodney and Cassandra are going to watch a film in which language?

....

85. In *The Unlucky Winner Is...* what is the brand name of the cereal flakes hosting the painting competition?

a) Fab Flakes
b) Mega Flakes
c) Super Flakes ....

86. In *Yuppy Love* which apparently unsavoury club does Del bump into Mickey Pearce in?

....

87. In *The Unlucky Winner Is...* Del has got a date with a woman he chatted up at a boot sale. What is her name?

....

88. In *Yuppy Love* what of Del's does Rodney end up regretting chucking out with the rubbish?

....

89. What is the name of the Indian restaurant where Arnie has one of his 'heart attacks'?

a) The Star of Bengal
b) Tandoori Nights
c) The Light of Nepal ....

90. At the end of *Chain Gang* who drives the ambulance that takes Arnie away?

....

91. In *The Unlucky Winner Is...* who does Del buy Italian shirts made in Malaya from?

....

92. In *Sickness and Wealth* what does Boycie refer to the Trotters as when they enter the Nag's Head?

....

93. In the opening scene of *Little Problems* what is Mike about to eat when Boycie starts talking about wombs?

....

94. In *Sickness and Wealth* what is the name of the female doctor who examines Del?

....

95. In *The Unlucky Winner Is...* what does an embarrassed Rodney ask Del to buy for him?

....

96. In *The Unlucky Winner Is...* what type of championship has Rodney made it to the final of at the junior disco?

....

97. In *The Unlucky Winner Is...* Del claims there is a poster of which pop star in Rodney's hotel room?

a) Prince
b) Michael Jackson
c) MC Hammer ....

98. In *The Unlucky Winner Is...* how much money do the Trotters believe they have won on the Spanish lottery?

....

99. In *Yuppy Love* what does Del write in the collar of Rodney's coat?

....

100. In *Little Problems* how much money does Boycie suddenly 'discover' in his pocket after claiming he was skint?

a) £1,000
b) £2,000
c) £3,000 ....

★★★

SERIES SEVEN EPISODE GUIDE

Episode 1: The Sky's The Limit
When Del takes possession of a new satellite dish he believes he's on to a big earner. But it soon becomes clear that this particular dish definitely isn't picking up television signals...

First published: Sunday December 30th 1990 at 7.15pm.

Episode 2: The Chance Of A Lunchtime
When Raquel gets an audition for a play she starts dreaming of stardom and Del can't help but worry that all the codpieces and cravats are going to her head. That is until she receives some shocking but very good news.

First screened: Sunday January 6th 1991 at 7.15pm.

Episode 3: Stage Fright
When Del gets the opportunity to provide a cabaret act for the birthday of a local villain's mother, he's got the perfect duo in mind. Raquel and Trigger's council depot mate, Tony. Everything's cushty, until the truth about Tony's vocal wange is revealed...

First screened: Sunday January 13th 1991 at 7.15pm.

Episode 4: The Class Of '62
A surprise school reunion at the Nag's Head signals the return of Slater. But has he really changed? And is the reunion really just a chance to catch up with old 'mates'?

First screened: Sunday January 20th 1991 at 7.15pm.

Episode 5: He Ain't Heavy, He's My Uncle
When Del and Raquel become a two car family, Rodney finds new employment as Del's personal car cleaner. Meanwhile Albert falls victim to a gang of muggers on the estate. When Del eyes a suspicious mob in the Nag's Head he sees that justice is done.

First screened: Sunday January 27th 1991 at 7.15pm.

Episode 6: Three Men, A Woman, And A Baby
While Del is about to become a dad, Rodney makes one final attempt at patching things up with Cassandra. Amazingly it works, but just as Rodney and Cassandra start making up for lost time, Raquel goes into labour and Del insists Rodney is at the hospital when the baby is born.

First screened: Sunday February 3rd 1991 at 7.15pm.

QUIZ SEVEN - SERIES SEVEN

1. In *The Sky's The Limit* Albert brings Del two morning papers with a cup of tea. One is the Financial Times. What is the other?

....

2. What does the sign on Del's bedroom door read?

....

3. In *The Chance of A Lunchtime* what does Raquel reveal that her husband did for a living?

....

4. In *Stage Fright* Del claims that who is selling quality reject three-piece-suites?

....

5. In *The Class Of '62* what is the name of the class that is reunited?

a) Class 4A   b) Class 4B   c) Class 4C ....

6. What is the name of the school the reunited attended?

....

7. What was the school originally called?

....

118

8. What was the nickname of the school's one eared, and now incarcerated, headmaster?

....

9. In *He Ain't Heavy, He's My Uncle* whose mum is Albert trying to impress in the Nag's Head?

....

10. In *Three Men, A Woman and A Baby* which tourist attraction does Rodney take Cassandra to?

....

11. In *The Sky's The Limit* what is the nickname of the painter and decorator working at Boycie's house?

....

12. What relation is he to Boycie?

....

13. In *Stage Fright* what is the name of the club that needs a singing act for the birthday of a local villain's mother?

....

The Official Only Fools and Horses Quiz Book

14. What is the villain's full name?

....

15. According to rumour, who pays him protection money?

....

16. What is his mother's name?

....

17. What is the name of the club's manager?

....

18. In *The Chance Of A Lunchtime* Raquel is rehearsing for an audition of which Shakespeare play?

a) Much Ado About Nothing
b) A Midsummer Night's Dream
c) As You Like It ....

19. For which part is she auditioning?

....

20. What is the name of the play's director?

....

44. In what prison did Slater do time for diamond smuggling?

a) Wandsworth
b) Parkhurst
c) Wormwood Scrubs ....

45. According to Slater, who did he 'find' in prison?

....

46. Since leaving prison what has Slater been working as?

....

47. In *The Chance Of A Lunchtime* what is the name of the drunken woman in the Nag's Head who turns out to be an ex fiancée of Del's?

....

48. In *He Ain't Heavy, He's My Uncle* what is the name of the greaser Del pays to beat up the gang of skinheads in the Nag's Head?

....

49. Who do the gang of skinheads turn out to actually be?

....

The Official Only Fools and Horses Quiz Book

50. According to Uncle Albert what kind of animal did he once come face to face with in an African jungle?

a) Rhino **b)** Lion **c)** Elephant ....

51. In *The Sky's The Limit*, what, according to Mike, were Rodney, Mickey Pearce and Jevon pretending to be in the Nag's Head the night before?

....

52. What is the name of the club where Del and Rodney first see Tony Angelino perform?

....

53. According to Trigger what does Tony do for a living?

....

54. In *The Class Of '62* Del and his mates look at an old photo of themselves in the school football team. What position did Del play?

a) Defence **b)** Midfield **c)** Attack ....

55. What position did Denzil play?

....

56. Who played at left back?

a) Albie Littlewood
b) Jumbo Mills
c) Monkey Harris ....

57. Del likens his playing style to Paul Gascoigne's. Who does he say Boycie played like?

....

58. In *The Sky's The Limit* the radar transmitter dish on the Trotter's balcony was stolen from which airport?

a) Heathrow **b)** Stansted **c)** Gatwick ....

59. In *A Chance Of A Lunchtime* Albert mentions a naval chief communications officer who died when he dropped a depth charge in nine feet of water. What was his name?

....

60. In *Stage Fright* with who have Tony and Raquel apparently just finished a sell-out season in Las Vegas?

....

61. What is the title of the first song that Raquel and Tony sing?

....

62. According to Raquel, she and Tony sang three more songs after Del left. Name two of them.

....

63. Tony Angelino claims he is a victim of which 'ism'?

....

64. In *The Sky's The Limit*, where, according to Del, does Rodney look like he's just been on an 18-30 holiday to?

....

65. In *He Ain't Heavy, He's My Uncle* which birthday is Boycie and Marlene's son about to celebrate?

a) 1st **b)** 2nd **c)** 3rd ....

66. In *Three Men, A Woman and A Baby* what does Trigger buy from Del 'in case of an emergency'?

....

67. In *The Chance Of A Lunchtime* which country's national anthem plays when Rodney rings the Trotter's doorbell?

a) France
b) America
c) Germany ....

128

68. In *The Sky's The Limit* what does Del order with his Peach Daiquiri?

....

69. What name does Slater know Raquel by?

....

70. In *The Sky's The Limit* what is the name of the discreet concierge at the hotel where Rodney plans to surprise Cassandra with a second honeymoon?

....

71. Before doing business with Del what is the most amount of money Tony Angelino has ever been paid for a gig?

a) £50 **b)** £80 **c)** £100 ....

72. In *The Sky's The Limit* what city is Cassandra's flight home re-routed to?

a) Liverpool
b) Manchester
c) Leeds ....

The Official Only Fools and Horses Quiz Book

73. In *Stage Fright* what is the name of the local hall where Raquel and Tony rehearse for their big night?

....

74. In *The Chance Of A Lunchtime*, where, according to Del, is the restaurant Cassandra has asked Rodney to meet her at?

....

75. Slater once planted three thousand what on Trigger?

....

76. What is the brand name of the wigs Del is selling in *Three Men, A Woman and A Baby*?

....

77. Whose nephew, from the Bangladeshi butchers, did Del buy the wigs from?

....

78. In *The Chance Of A Lunchtime* what is the name of the camp set designer Del gets stuck with in a wine bar?

....

79. In *Stage Fright* how long does Raquel say that she and her husband have been separated?

a) 7 years **b)** 8 years **c)** 9 years ....

80. In *He Ain't Heavy, He's My Uncle* Del buys what kind of car for Raquel?

a) Ford Cortina
b) Ford Capri
c) Ford Escort ....

81. What colour is the car

a) Green
b) Pink
c) Yellow ....

82. By which nickname does Rodney refer to the car?

....

83. How much does Del pay for the car?

a) £100
b) £250
c) £400 ....

LOVELY JUBBLY

84. In *He Ain't Heavy, He's My Uncle* who brings Albert's pocket watch back?

....

85. In *Stage Fright* what is Del in court for?

....

CHRISTMAS SPECIALS

★★★★★★★★★★★

1985 - 1991

CHRISTMAS SPECIALS (1985 - 1991) EPISODE GUIDE

To Hull And Back
The Trotters move into the diamond smuggling business, but how are they going to get to Holland and back with Slater and his cronies keeping a watch on all the major airports?

First screened: Wednesday December 25th 1985 at 7.30pm.

☆ ☆ ☆

A Royal Flush
When Rodney befriends a posh girl in the market, the Trotters end up rubbing shoulders with royalty. Things are looking up, as long as Del can resist his habit of interfering.

First screened: Thursday December 25th 1986 at 7.05pm.

☆ ☆ ☆

The Frog's Legacy
At the wedding of Trigger's niece his Aunt Reenie tells Del and Rodney about their mum's old friend Freddie The Frog. Rodney wants to know why this charming villain left his ill-gotten gains to the Trotters and why everyone notes his resemblance to him. Del is more interested in what happened to his hoard of gold bullion.

First screened: Friday December 25th 1987 at 6.25pm.

☆ ☆ ☆

Dates
When Del joins a dating agency he finds true romance in budding actress, Raquel. All is running smoothly until the strip-o-gram he hires for Albert's birthday bash turns up.

First screened: Sunday December 25th 1988 at 5.05pm.

The Jolly Boys' Outing
Del and the lads head off on a beano to the seaside. On the down side, the coach explodes and there's a rail strike. On the up side, Del is unexpectedly reunited with the love of his life, Raquel.

First screened: Monday December 25th 1989 at 4.05pm.

Rodney Come Home
With a new wife, flat and job, things should be all rosy for Rodney. But married life isn't all he'd hoped it would be and he ends up kipping on Del's sofa. With the help of Del, things can only go from bad to worse.

First screened: Tuesday December 25th 1990 at 5.10pm.

Miami Twice: Part one: The American Dream
When Rodney receives an unexpected windfall, Del kindly uses the money to buy Rodney and Cassandra two non-refundable tickets for a holiday in Miami. The problem is Cassandra has an important bank seminar to attend that very week. What are the odds?

First screened: Tuesday December 24th 1991 at 7.30 pm.

135

The Official Only Fools and Horses Quiz Book

Miami Twice: Part two: Oh To Be In England
With Del taking Cassandra's place, the Trotter Brothers take on Miami. But taking on the local mafia family was not part of their holiday plans.

First screened: Wednesday December 25th 1991 at 3.10pm.

QUIZ EIGHT
CHRISTMAS SPECIALS (1985 - 1991)

1. In *To Hull And Back* Rodney is trying to tell Del Boy about a girlfriend who is becoming too serious. What is her name?

....

2. In *The Frog's Legacy* what is the brand name of the computers Del is struggling to sell?

....

3. In *Miami Twice* what is the name of the Italian restaurant where Del narrowly dodges a bullet?

a) Carluccio's
b) Capello's
c) Carlotti's ....

4. In *A Royal Flush* what is Vicky selling in the market when Rodney first meets her?

....

5. Name two of the famous art institutes Vicky claims to have studied at?

....

6. What is the name of Vicky's family home?

....

The Official Only Fools and Horses Quiz Book

7. In *The Jolly Boys' Outing* what type of infection is Denzil taking antibiotics for?

....

8. In *To Hull And Back* what rank in the police force has Slater been promoted to?

a) Detective inspector
b) Chief detective inspector
c) Superintendent ....

9. In *Miami Twice* what is crucially wrong with the 'Trotter's Pre-blessed Wine'?

....

10. What country is the wine from?

....

11. According to the reverend, Raquel may be getting a call from which religious figure's office?

....

12. In *To Hull And Back* Denzil has got himself a new job as what?

....

13. In *Dates* what is the name of the dating agency Del (and Trigger) use?

....

14. In order to 'add a bit of glamour' what did Trigger tell the agency his job was?

....

15. In *Rodney Come Home* what does Uncle Albert accidentally set fire to?

....

16. In *To Hull And Back* what is the name of the old lady Albert watches a film with in the Nag's Head?

....

17. In *A Royal Flush* Del claims the canteen of cutlery he is selling is made of steel from which country?

....

18. In *The Frog's Legacy* Del gets Rodney a job as a what?

....

19. In *Dates* Mickey Pearce and who else encourage Rodney to get a date with the Nag's Head barmaid?

....

The Official Only Fools and Horses Quiz Book

20. What is the barmaid's full name?

....

21. Unbeknown to Rodney, what is her nickname?

....

22. In *The Jolly Boys' Outing* what is the name of the car radios Del is selling?

....

23. What country were the radios made in?

....

24. Which female pop star's LP is Del giving away free with the radios?

....

25. In *Rodney Come Home* what is the name of Rodney's new secretary?

....

26. In *Miami Twice* what is the name of the nightclub where Del and Rodney first meet the mafia?

....

140

27. In *To Hull And Back* Del, Boycie and Abdul hold a secret meeting in which dark and secluded location?

....

28. In *A Royal Flush* what country does Vicky say her mother was in when she died in a skiing accident?

a) Switzerland
b) France
c) Austria ....

29. According to Trigger's aunt, Reenie, approximately how much gold bullion did Freddie the Frog and his gang steal from the city bank?

a) £100,000
b) £250,000
c) £500,000 ....

30. What alias, and anagram of his own name, did Freddie the Frog use when ordering the coffin for the stolen gold?

....

31. In *Dates* Del likens himself to which Bonanza character?

....

32. In *The Jolly Boys' Outing* which board game is played at Rodney and Cassandra's anniversary dinner?

....

33. According to Del, what three letter word is a female swan?

....

34. In *Miami Twice* which famous entrepreneur does Del accuse of pushing in at the airport departure gate?

....

35. In *Rodney Come Home* Raquel admits to Del that she has a fear of what?

a) Spiders
b) The dark
c) Heights ....

36. In *To Hull And Back* how much does Rodney have to pay at a toll booth, despite his van having only three wheels?

....

37. What is Vicky's father the Duke of?

a) Malvern
b) Maylebury
c) Marlborough...

38. What is the name of the Duke's butler?

a) Wallace
b) Jones
c) Patterson ....

39. In *The Jolly Boys' Outing* what is the name of the halfway house the coach stops at?

....

40. What is the full name of the ex publican Mike introduces Del to in the halfway house toilets?

....

41. In *Dates* Del threatens to tell Marlene about a mistress of Boycie's who lives in which city?

a) Manchester
b) Leeds
c) Sheffield ....

42. In *Rodney Come Home* what country has Raquel just returned from?

....

43. While there she was doing a tour of which musical?

....

44. In *To Hull And Back* what is the name of the cafe in Hull where Denzil stops for breakfast?

....

45. In *To Hull And Back* how much money does Del throw off the balcony?

a) £10,000
b) £15,000
c) £20,000 ....

46. In *A Royal Flush* what is the name of the tout Del gets opera tickets from?

....

47. Which opera are the tickets for?

a) The Barber Of Seville
b) Carmen
c) La Boheme ....

48. Del brings ex girlfriend, June, to the opera. What is June's surname?

....

49. In *To Hull And Back* Slater writes a suspect list. Who of the following is **not** on the list?

a) Sunglasses Ron
b) Ronnie Nelson
c) Monkey Harris ....

50. In *Dates* Del takes Raquel for lunch at which London hotel?

a) The Hilton
b) The Dorchester
c) The Savoy ....

51. In *The Jolly Boys' Outing* what is the name of Cassandra's yuppy boss?

a) Simon
b) Adrian
c) Stephen ....

52. What is his wife's name?

a) Chloe
b) Stephanie
c) Joanne ....

53. In *Rodney Come Home* which pop star's LP has Rodney bought Cassandra for her birthday?

....

54. He also got her some earrings. What, according to Rodney, was wrong with them?

....

55. In *Miami Twice* what type of large reptile do Del and Rodney come across whilst on the run in the Everglades?

a) Alligator
b) Snake
c) Crocodile ....

56. What is the name of the boat the Trotters use to sail to Holland and back?

....

57. In The *Frog's Legacy* the Trotters are invited to a wedding in which county?

....

58. As a wedding present the Trotters have bought a dinner service containing how many pieces?

a) 12 **b)** 13 **c)** 24 ....

59. In *The Jolly Boys' Outing* who is originally put in charge of the sandwiches?

....

60. What is the nickname of Del's mafia Don double, Vinny Ochetti?

a) The Snake
b) The Chain
c) The Blade ....

61. What is the name of Don Ochetti's son?

....

62. In *To Hull And Back* what does Slater wear to disguise himself as a holiday maker?

....

63. In *A Royal Flush* which 'boring' county does Vicky say she was brought up in?

....

64. What is the name of the race horse owned by Vicky's father?

....

65. In *To Hull And Back* how much money is Del originally offered to go to Amsterdam?

....

FOR SALE

147

66. In *To Hull And Back* what is Del Boy trying to sell to a customer in the Nag's Head?

....

67. In *The Frog's Legacy* what is Del trying to sell in the market with the help of a tap-dancing Uncle Albert?

....

68. In *The Jolly Boys' Outing* what is the name of the first guest house the Trotters try to stay in?

....

69. What is the name of the elderly lady who owns the guest house?

a) Mrs Baker
b) Mrs Butler
c) Mrs Butcher ....

70. Mickey Pearce, Jevon and who else are staying at the guest house?

....

71. What is the name of the spooky B&B the Trotters end up booking a room in?

....

72. What is the B&B's lady owner called?

....

73. What is the name of the Irish waitress who shows the Trotters to their room?

....

74. In *Dates* Raquel is offered a dance tour of which part of the world?

....

75. In *To Hull And Back* which Dutch football team's name does Del shout to passers by on the North Sea canal?

....

76. In *The Jolly Boys' Outing* what is the name of the coach driver who is overcome by fumes?

....

77. Who takes his place behind the wheel?

....

78. What is the first name of Slater's assistant, Hoskins?

....

79. In *To Hull And Back* what does Slater claim Del once put in his school milk?

....

80. In *To Hull And Back* what aftershave does a spruced up Trigger claim to be wearing in the Nag's Head?

....

81. In *To Hull And Back* what show does Uncle Albert try to find on the ship's radio?

....

82. Where did Freddie the Frog bury the stolen gold bullion?

....

83. In *To Hull And Back* what is wrong with the £50,000 Boycie and Abdul use to buy the diamonds?

....

84. In *To Hull And Back*, apart from Del Boy, Trigger and Denzil, name two of the three other suspects on Slater's list?

....

85. What reason for elimination does Slater write next to Denzil's name on the list?

....

86. In *Dates* which Hollywood actor's 'look' does Rodney attempt to copy to impress his date?

....

87. In *The Jolly Boys' Outing* Raquel is working as an assistant to a magician called Ray. What is Ray's stage name?

....

88. In *Miami Twice* which Bee Gee makes a cameo appearance?

a) Barry Gibb
b) Maurice Gibb
c) Robin Gibb ....

89. Which Bee Gee hit does Del sing at him?

a) Night Fever
b) Words
c) How deep is your love? ....

90. In *To Hull And Back* what is the first name of the Dutch diamond dealer, Van Kleefe?

....

91. In *Dates* what secret society does Del try to join in order to help Raquel?

....

92. In *The Jolly Boys' Outing* Cassandra receives a call from the police constabulary of which county?

a) Essex
b) Kent
c) Sussex ....

93. In *Miami Twice* what is the name of the church where Damien is christened?

a) The Parish Church of Peckham
b) Our Lady of the Divine Rosemary
c) St Mary's ....

94. Who is the photographer at Damien's christening?

....

95. In *To Hull And Back* what is the name of Abdul's diamond expert cousin?

....

96. In *The Jolly Boys' Outing* who becomes unwell after 'copping an unfortunate whelk'?

....

97. In *To Hull And Back* what is the 6 digit combination to Boycie's briefcase?

....

98. In *Miami Twice* who does Del pay to baby sit Damien?

....

99. In *Miami Twice* what is the full name of the Colombian drug baron who mistakes Del for Don Ochetti?

....

100. In *The Jolly Boys' Outing* what does Uncle Albert claim froze when he was on the Russian convoys?

....

101. In *To Hull And Back* which of Boycie's unhappy customers has broken down on the A1?

....

102. In *The Jolly Boys' Outing* what is Trigger upset about losing?

....

103. In *Rodney Come Home* what is the name of the receptionist of the exhaust centre that Rodney asks out on a date?

....

104. Rodney plans to take her to the cinema to see what film?

....

105. In *Miami Twice* Cassandra cannot go to Miami because she has to attend the bank's seminar in which seaside town?

a) Worthing
b) Eastbourne
c) Brighton ....

106. In *To Hull And Back* which airport does Slater spend 18 hours at?

....

107. In *The Jolly Boys' Outing* what is the name of the club where Del meets Raquel again?

....

108. In *The Jolly Boys' Outing* with what does Rodney 'assault' a police officer?

....

109. In *Miami Twice* Rodney agrees to stay in the camper van with Del on the condition that he doesn't eat what?

....

110. In *To Hull And Back* how many diamonds do the Trotters smuggle back into the country?

....

111. In *Miami Twice* Del's jet ski runs out of gas 35 miles off the coast of which Caribbean Island?

a) Cuba
b) Puerto Rico
c) Trinidad ....

112. In *To Hull And Back* what is the name of the Dutch bank where Van Kleefe and his 'money' are found out?

....

113. In *A Royal Flush* what type of gun does Del use at the clay pigeon shoot?

a) Uzi
b) Tommy Gun
c) Pump-action shotgun ....

114. Del has borrowed the gun from which bank robbing associate?

....

115. In *Dates* what surname does Del use at the dating agency?

....

116. In *The Jolly Boys' Outing* who does Rodney punch on the nose?

....

117. In *To Hull And Back* what type of bird does Rodney do a less than impressive impersonation of?

....

118. In *Miami Twice* what is the name of Don Ochetti's ever nervous lawyer?

....

119. In *A Royal Flush* how much money does the Duke offer Rodney to stay away from Vicky?

a) £1,000
b) £2,000
c) £3,000 ....

120. In *Dates* Raquel's flat is in which road?

....

121. In *To Hull And Back* what is the name of the police constable who accompanies Slater and Hoskins to investigate a disturbance in Soweto Road?

....

122. In *The Jolly Boys' Outing* Boycie and who else were hit by a flying suitcase?

....

123. In *Miami Twice* what is the nickname of the mafia henchman who breaks into the Trotter's camper van?

....

124. To which seaside resort do the jolly boys go on a beano?

a) Southend
b) Ramsgate
c) Margate ....

125. In *To Hull And Back* what is the name of the Rastafarian who apologises to Del for spilling his lager on the Nag's Head bar?

....

126. In *To Hull And Back* what nickname does Slater claim the metropolitan police have given him?

a) Pit-bull
b) Bull dog
c) Rottweiler ....

127. In *Miami Twice* what sport do Del and Rodney play in the grounds of Don Ochetti's mansion?

....

128. In *To Hull And Back* what star constellation do the completely lost at sea Trotters look for in the night sky?

....

159

129. Unable to find it, Albert is very excited, however, when he spots what?

....

130. In *Rodney Come Home* who is Del Boy's new look-out?

....

★ ★ ★

CHRISTMAS SPECIALS

1992 - 2003

CHRISTMAS SPECIALS (1992 - 2003) EPISODE GUIDE

Mother Nature's son

When Del 'discovers' his very own water spring, the money starts rolling in for the Trotters. But how long will it be before the true source of Del's 'spring' is discovered.

First screened: Friday December 25th 1992 at 6.55pm.

Fatal Extraction

After Del falls back into his old ways of drinking and gambling till dawn, Raquel leaves him. Undeterred, Del decides to see if he can still pull and gets a date with a dental receptionist. Realising his mistake, he cancels the date and gets back with Raquel. But he can't help but feel he is being followed…

First screened: Saturday December 25th 1993 at 6.05 pm.

Heroes And Villains

Whilst Cassandra has a knackered Rodney on a gruelling baby-making programme, Del has his eye on the first prize of a publican's fancy dress ball. When the pair inadvertently become street vigilantes they find that being on the right side of the law for once has its advantages.

First screened: Wednesday December 25th 1996 at 9.00pm.

Modern Men

Del's been reading a new man's guide to the 21st century, but Raquel hasn't seen much improvement. Meanwhile Rodney and Cassandra face heartache when she has a miscarriage.

First screened: Friday December 27th 1996 at 8.00pm.

☆ ☆☆

Time On Our Hands

With Rodney still hurting over his and Cassandra's loss, it falls to Del to get him to open up. Meanwhile the discovery of an old watch in the Trotter's garage should earn them a few quid. Actually, as they discover at auction, it's worth quite a bit more…

First screened: Sunday December 29th 1996 at 8.00pm.

☆ ☆☆

If They Could See Us Now

The Trotters enjoy their newly acquired millions in style, and it's just as well, as with Del and Rodney in charge of stocks and shares investments, it could never really last. Back in Peckham , Del sees a new game show as the answer to all their prayers…

First screened: Tuesday December 25th 2001 at 9.05pm.

☆ ☆☆

The Official Only Fools and Horses Quiz Book

Strangers On The Shore
Del and Rodney say goodbye to the recently deceased Uncle Albert and decide to attend a naval reunion in France in his honour. But on their return to Peckham they discover that cheap booze isn't the only thing they've brought back with them…

First screened: Wednesday December 25th 2002 at 9.40pm.

☆ ☆☆

Sleepless In Peckham
Just as the bankrupt Trotters face ruin, Uncle Albert's will saves the day. Meanwhile as Cassandra is about to give birth, Rodney discovers an old photograph that finally reveals the truth about his parentage.

First screened: Thursday December 25th 2003 at 9.20pm.

☆ ☆☆

QUIZ NINE
CHRISTMAS SPECIALS (1992 - 2003)

1. In *Mother Nature's Son* what name is inscribed on the 9 carat identity bracelet in Del's stock?

....

2. In *Modern Men* what medical procedure does Del 'positively' decide to undergo?

....

3. In *Fatal Extraction*, what, to his horror, does Del find boiling in a pot on the kitchen stove?

....

4. In *Heroes and Villains* Del has bought a load of radio alarm clocks that go off whenever they like. Where were they made?

a) Latvia
b) Estonia
c) Lithuania ....

5. In *Time On Our Hands* an associate of Del's is selling 250 electric carpet steamers. What is his name?

....

6. In *Strangers On The Shore* which of Del's associates is selling log effect gas fires?

....

165

The Official Only Fools and Horses Quiz Book

7. Where were they made?

a) Slovakia
b) Estonia
c) Latvia ....

8. In *If They Could See Us Now* who is in prison for embezzlement?

....

9. In *Sleepless In Peckham* what type of cosmetic surgery does Marlene undergo?

a) Nose job
b) Tummy tuck
c) Boob job ....

10. In *Fatal Extraction* what is the name of the song a drunken Del sings that causes a full scale riot on the estate?

....

11. What type of gear does Del sell to the rioters?

....

12. In *Mother Nature's Son* Del receives a summons ordering him to clear up whose old allotment?

....

13. In *If They Could See Us Now* Rodney attempts to spice up his and Cassandra's love life by dressing up as what?

....

14. What does Cassandra dress up as?

....

15. In *Modern Men* Del sports a pair of bright green satin pyjamas. Who did he buy them from?

....

16. In *Strangers On The Shore*, what, according to Marlene, has she spent the last five years trying to convince her mum that Boycie is not?

....

17. In *Time On Our Hands* Del claims that he is well in with the manager of which local restaurant?

....

18. In *Fatal Extraction* which record by Mike Oldfield did Del buy Raquel for Christmas?

....

19. In *Mother Nature's Son*, what, according to Trigger, is his new job title?

....

20. In *Heroes and Villains* what kind of pet does Rodney get for a brooding Cassandra?

....

21. What do they call the pet?

....

22. In *Sleepless In Peckham*, after no one has seen either of them for ten days, who does Del suspect Marlene has run off with?

....

23. In *Modern Men* Del has a new idea for a company with the initials TCT. What does TCT stand for?

....

24. In *Sleepless In Peckham* what is the name of the David Bowie tribute act that plays in the Nag's Head?

....

25. In *Time On Our Hands* what does Albert mistake for gravy?

....

26. In *Mother Nature's Son* whose van does Del use to get rid of drums of toxic waste?

....

27. What kind of outfit does Del wear when transporting the toxic waste?

....

28. In the opening scene of *Modern Men* what is the name of the champagne the Trotters are celebrating with?

....

29. In *If They Could See Us Now* who is Uncle Albert living with?

....

30. In *Heroes and Villains* Trigger has been awarded a medal for having the same broom for how many years?

a) 10 **b)** 15 **c)** 20 ....

31. Although Trigger claims to have had the same broom for all this time, he also admits that it has had:

a) 15 new heads and 13 new handles?
b) 17 new heads and 14 new handles?
c) 19 new heads and 15 new handles? ....

32. In *Time On Our Hands* what name is inscribed on the pocket watch found in the Trotter's garage?

....

33. What did Del originally believe the pocket watch to be?

....

34. In *If They Could See Us Now* what is the name of the quiz show Del appears on?

....

35. Who is the host of the show?

....

36. In *Sleepless In Peckham* who is suspected of being murdered?

....

37. In *Mother Nature's Son* what is the name of the 'mineral' water the Trotters are selling?

....

38. Who advises Del to advertise his new water business on local radio?

....

39. In *Fatal Extraction* Del and Rodney gamble till dawn at which club?

....

40. According to Del who owns the club?

a) Eugene McCarthy
b) Ronnie Nelson
c) The Driscoll brothers ....

41. What is the name of the club's barman?

a) Orlando
b) Miguel
c) Enrico ....

42. In *Time On Our Hands* what is the make of the car that Rodney buys for Del?

a) Bentley
b) Aston Martin
c) Rolls Royce ....

43. What does the personalised number plate on Del's new car read?

....

44. In *Strangers On The Shore* which two Nag's Head regulars do Del and Rodney 'mysteriously' bump into in a French hypermarket?

....

45. In the opening scene of *Heroes and Villains* Rodney has a futuristic dream set in what year?

a) 2026
b) 2036
c) 2056 ....

46. In *If They Could See Us Now* who makes a prank phone call to Rodney pretending to be the Sultan of Brunei?

....

47. In *Mother Nature's Son* what is the name of the health food centre where Rodney gets his and Cassandra's shopping?

....

48. What is the name of the friend of the earth and self made millionaire who owns the centre?

....

49. In *If They Could See Us Now* where are the Trotters on holiday?

a) St Tropez
b) Cannes
c) Monte Carlo ....

50. What is the name of the hotel the Trotters are staying in?

....

51. In *Modern Men* what is the title of the book Del is reading?

....

52. In *Fatal Extraction* who does Del buy 650 military camcorders from?

a) Ugandan Morris
b) Sunglasses Ron
c) Ronnie Nelson ....

53. Where were the camcorders made?

a) Russia
b) North Korea
c) Afghanistan ....

54. In *Mother Nature's Son* the Trotters have a weekend away in which seaside resort?

a) Brighton
b) Bournemouth
c) Blackpool ....

55. What famous hotel do they stay in?

....

56. In *Time On Our Hands* what does graffiti in the Nelson Mandela House lift claim that Del is?

....

57. In *Strangers On The Shore* what do Del and Rodney name their new illegal immigrant 'friend'?

....

58. In *If They Could See Us Now* what is the name of the Trotter's barrister?

....

59. In *Heroes and Villains* what does Uncle Albert mistake for apple juice?

....

60. In *Strangers On The Shore* a letter arrives for Albert inviting him to a reunion for the crew of which ship?

....

61. What is the name of the French village where the reunion is being held?

....

62. What is the defining physical feature of most of the village's male residents?

....

63. Only one crew member is present at the reunion. What is his full name?

....

64. In *Fatal Extraction* what does Denzil find in his porridge at the cafe?

....

65. In *Modern Men* Mickey Pearce has got a new job as what?

....

66. Part of his new job is recruitment. Where does he hold the interviews?

....

67. In *Sleepless In Peckham* what embarrassing medical condition has Denzil had surgery for?

....

68. In *Modern Men* what is the name of the angry Sikh doctor Del is trying to avoid?

....

69. What is the doctor's nickname?

....

70. According to Rodney the paint they used to decorate the doctors surgery should have been used by...?

a) 1983
b) 1985
c) 1987 ....

71. In *Strangers On The Shore* what does Del name the extra strong curry that he makes?

....

72. In *Mother Nature's Son* which two 'specialists' does Del pay to clear the allotment?

....

73. In *Strangers On The Shore* what does Del put in Boycie's hair gel?

....

The Official Only Fools and Horses Quiz Book

74. In *Time On Our Hands* the pocket watch is sold at which London auction house?

a) Bonham's
b) Christie's
c) Sotheby's ....

75. How much does the pocket watch sell for?

a) £6.2 million
b) £6.3 million
c) £6.4 million ....

76. In *Sleepless In Peckham* Del suggests Rodney write a Harry Potter style book called what?

....

77. In *Time On Our Hands* what is the name of the boat Del buys for Uncle Albert?

....

78. In *Fatal Extraction* what kind of pet does Del get Damien for Christmas?

a) Gerbil
b) Hamster
c) Guinea Pig ....

79. What is the pet's name?

....

80. What does a panicking Rodney mistake it for?

....

81. In *Modern Men* who ends up in casualty after using one of Del Boy's hair dryers?

....

82. What, in fact, are the hair dryers?

....

83. In *If They Could See Us Now* who is the new manager of the Nag's Head?

....

84. In *Heroes and Villains* what is the full name of the late publican whose turn it is to hold an annual fancy dress ball?

....

85. What is the name of the pub that he ran?

....

86. What crime fighting duo do Del and Rodney go dressed as?

....

87. Who did Rodney originally suggest they go as?

a) Laurel and Hardy
b) Butch Cassidy and the Sundance Kid
c) The Blues Brothers ....

88. Who does Trigger mistake them for?

....

89. What does Trigger go to the 'ball' dressed as?

....

90. In *Sleepless In Peckham* what does Trigger 'invent' with the help of two chopsticks?

....

91. In *Fatal Extraction* what is the name of the dental receptionist Del asks out on a date?

....

92. In *Strangers On The Shore* who is Del working for as a chauffeur?

....

93. In *Heroes and Villains* what type of personally inscribed present does Del get Rodney for his birthday?

....

94. What does the inscription say?

....

95. In *Mother Nature's Son* part of Del's stock is a plate commemorating whose wedding?

....

96. After finally becoming millionaires, the Trotters get a round of applause in the Nag's Head. Who starts the applause?

....

97. At the end of *Time On Our Hands* Del tells Rodney that he has booked them all a holiday to where?

....

98. In *Fatal Extraction* what type of ache is Del Boy suffering with?

a) Back ache
b) Ear ache
c) Toothache ....

99. At the end of *Time On Our Hands* what game does a bored Del play in his new country mansion?

....

100. In *Strangers On The Shore* where has Damien hidden Cassandra's birth control pills?

....

101. In *Mother Nature's Son* in what location does the 'spring' spring up?

....

102. In *Fatal Extraction* Raquel leaves Del. Who do she and Damien go to stay with?

....

103. In *Sleepless In Peckham* who does Rodney discover is his real father?

....

104. In *Sleepless in Peckham* how much money does Uncle Albert leave Del and Rodney each in his will?

....

105. What does Rodney name his and Cassandra's baby girl?

....

★ ★ ★

QUIZ TEN – GENERAL KNOWLEDGE

1. Who does Del Boy always support in the university boat race?

....

2. What relation is Uncle Albert to Grandad?

....

3. What is the name of Albert's estranged and embittered wife?

....

4. Rodney once went on a date with a Southern area shot-put champion. What was her nickname?

....

5. What did Trigger's mum put under father's name on his birth certificate?

....

6. What is Trigger's aunt Reenie's surname?

....

7. What was Freddie the Frog's surname?

....

8. What is Raquel's favourite film?

....

9. In series six a poster advertising a bull fight features on the Trotter's kitchen door. What is the matador's name?

....

10. According to Mike, the Nag's Head is built on a public grave for victims of what disease?

....

11. What is Cassandra's middle name?

....

12. What is the name of Boycie and Marlene's son?

....

13. What affectionate abbreviation of his name does Cassandra call Rodney?

....

14. What was the name of the stall Del and Jumbo set up outside the Nag's Head?

....

15. What town does Raquel's brother live in?

a) Milton Keynes
b) Stevenage
c) Basingstoke ....

16. In which country do Cassandra's parents own a holiday villa?

a) Italy
b) Spain
c) Portugal ....

17. According to Uncle Albert how old was his father when he died?

....

18. What is Marlene's brother known as?

....

19. What does he do for a living?

....

20. What, according to a psychiatrist, does he suffer from?

....

21. What is Marlene's maiden name?

....

22. What kind of business does Cassandra's dad own?

....

23. What is Del and Raquel's song?

....

24. Who of the following has **not** been to prison?

a) Boycie **b)** Del **c)** Trigger ....

25. Who of the following did **not** go to school with Del?

a) Boycie   **b)** Trigger   **c)** Mike ....

26. According to Denzil, how old was he when he moved to London?

....

27. What is Marlene's mum's name?

....

28. What was the name of the street Uncle Albert was born in?

....

The Official Only Fools and Horses Quiz Book

29. Who are Damien's Godparents?

a) Boycie and Marlene
b) Rodney and Cassandra
c) Mickey Pearce and Jevon ....

30. Who was doing detention in the school's science lab when Del Boy blew it up?

a) Trigger
b) Albie Littlewood
c) Denzil ....

31. According to Del how old was Rodney when he stopped breast feeding?

....

32. According to Rodney what is the only thing Albert has ever grown?

....

33. According to Raquel her clothes only look fashionable when she is watching which TV channel?

....

34. How much did Damien weigh when he was born?

a) 7lbs   b) 8lbs   c) 9lbs ....

35. According to Albert, what once tried to have sex with the submarine he was on in the Barents Sea?

....

36. According to Trigger, what saying has been handed down through generations of road sweepers?

....

37. What does Raquel's dad do for a living?

....

38. What associate of Del's was deported along with a load of nine carat gold identity bracelets?

....

39. According to Del, who was the head boy at his school?

....

40. What are the names of Raquel's parents?

a) James and Audrey
b) Mark and Pam
c) David and Vivian ....

41. According to Trigger, who made one great film and was never seen again?

....

42. What nationality was Sid's wife?

....

43. According to Raquel, women are from Venus, men are from where?

....

44. In what episode do we first see Boycie?

....

45. In what series does Mickey Pearce first appear?

....

46. In which episode does Raquel announce that she is pregnant?

....

47. How many episodes does Roy Slater appear in?

....

48. In which two episodes does Del Boy get arrested?

....

49. In which two episodes does Rodney get arrested?

....

50. In which two episodes does Grandad get arrested?

....

51. What animal is Trigger named after?

....

52. Which of Del's associates owns a stationery shop in the high street?

....

53. Which football team did Reg Trotter say would one day win the cup?

....

54. What was the name of the church at which Joan and Reg got married?

....

55. How many times was Trigger's gran married?

a) One
b) Two
c) Three   ....

56. What was Joan Trotter's favourite colour?

....

57. Which brand of cigarettes did Del used to deliver
around Lewisham?

....

58. Which of Del's associates gets a discount at Hatton
Garden?

....

59. What is the name of the Trotter family doctor?

....

60. What was Joan's favourite flower?

....

61. At school who did Del sit next to in class?

....

62. Who did Slater once catch behind the school bike sheds with Del?

....

63. What is the name of Trigger's tomboy cousin?

....

64. Which singer does Reg Trotter do impressions of?

....

65. Who did Del describe as being his "bestest" friend?

....

66. In what county did Freddie the Frog own a holiday chalet?

....

67. Which of Del's associates owned a Cash and Carry and went on to own the 121 club?

....

68. Joan Trotter was a fan of which football club?

....

69. Where on her body does Marlene have a tattoo of a heart with a dagger going through it?

....

70. What did the 'A's on Del's O-level results stand for?

....

71. In which episode did Denzil first appear?

....

72. True or false? Del cannot swim.

....

73. True or false? Rodney is right handed.

....

74. True or false? Del once dated a life guard.

....

75. True or false? The Trotters live closer to the Nag's Head than Trigger does.

....

76. In what episode did Marlene make her first appearance?

....

77. What is the name of the block of flats the Trotters live in?

....

78. What floor do they live on?

a) 10th **b)** 11th **c)** 12th ....

79. How many television sets does Grandad normally watch?

....

80. What colour are the doors in the Trotter's flat from series 1 to 4?

....

81. What colour are the doors in the Trotter's flat from series 5 onwards?

....

82. What was The Advanced Electronics Research And Development Centre formerly known as?

....

193

The Official Only Fools and Horses Quiz Book

83. What are the names of Cassandra's parents?

a) John and Sharon
b) Alan and Pam
c) Kelvin and Janice ....

84. What is the name of Rodney's and Mickey Pearce's ladies hair stylist friend?

....

85. What is Joan Trotter's middle name?

....

86. What is the name of the African lady who lives in the flat directly beneath the Trotters?

....

87. Which of Del and Rodney's uncles was a tobacco baron?

....

88. What name does Trigger know Rodney by?

....

89. Who is Raquel's husband?

....

90. True or false? Rodney once went out with a Chinese girl.

....

91. True or false? Del once dated Marlene?

....

92. What 3 place names feature on the side of the Trotter's van?

a) Tokyo, New York, Peckham
b) Paris, Tokyo, Peckham
c) New York, Paris, Peckham ....

93. What is the name of the road Boycie and Marlene live in?

a) The Kings Way
b) The Kings Avenue
c) The Kings Lane ....

94. What is Uncle Albert's middle name?

....

95. Rodney has two GCEs. What subjects are they in?

a) Maths and English
b) Art and English
c) Maths and Art ....

96. True or false? Uncle Albert had a date with Petula?

....

97. What was the profession of Trigger's suicidal cousin, Cyril?

....

98. What is Damien's middle name?

a) Rodney   **b)** Derek   **c)** Troy ....

99. What is the name of Del's travel agent friend?

....

100. According to Del, what are the only two things in the world that frighten him?

....

101. In what kind of shop was Marlene working when she first met Boycie?

....

102. What was the profession of Marlene's dad?

....

103. Which of Del's associates is a gas fitter?

....

104. In what Series did Uncle Albert make his first appearance?

a) 2nd   **b)** 3rd   **c)** 4th ....

105. Which animal features in a painting that hangs over the Trotter's sofa throughout series 3 – 6?

....

106. Where was the art college that Rodney briefly attended?

....

107. Why was he expelled?

....

108. Who is Del Boy's Godfather?

....

109. How many brothers does Denzil have

a) 3   **b)** 4   **c)** 5 ....

The Official Only Fools and Horses Quiz Book

110. One of Denzil's brothers lives in Bethnal Green. What is his name?

....

111. Boycie once tried to bribe the Mayor of...?

a) Lewisham
b) Wandsworth
c) Lambeth ....

112. What was the title of the book Rodney once wrote?

....

113. Which of Del's associates runs a 'personal' shop down the Walworth Road?

....

114. Who was best man at Rodney and Cassandra's wedding?

a) Mickey Pearce
b) Del Boy
c) Jevon ....

115. Where did Rodney and Cassandra go for their honeymoon?

....

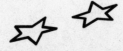

116. According to Del, his mum was the first woman in Peckham ever to smoke what kind of cigarettes?

....

117. True or False? Trigger once spent 22 months in a young offenders home.

....

118. What are the names of Roy Slater's parents?

a) Harry and Ruby
b) Johnny and Carol
c) Teddy and Linda ....

119. How old was Slater when he became a police officer?

a) 18   **b)** 19   **c)** 20 ....

120. How old was Uncle Albert when he joined the navy?

a) 17   **b)** 18   **c)** 19 ....

121. What is Raquel's surname?

....

122. According to Raquel, she once had a line in an episode of which TV show?

....

123. What was the name of the pop duo Raquel was once in?

....

124. According to Grandad what was the name of the friend he once tried to join the foreign legion with? (Full name)

....

125. Who did Slater once arrest for riding a bike with a defective rear light?

....

126. According to Del, who was still in borstal the last time Albert had his leg over?

....

127. True or false? As a kid, Del had three paper rounds.

....

128. What is the name of the Nag's Head barmaid Del refers to as a "saucy little cow"?

....

129. What did Del once sell to the West Indian lads at the youth centre as hats?

....

130. What was the name of the neighbour lady Del enlisted the help of to modify the hats?

....

131. What is the name of the Trotter's local pub?

....

132. According to rumour which of his relatives did Mickey Pearce once rob?

....

133. What is the name of the Trotter's local newspaper?

....

134. According to Rodney, Freddie the Frog was also known by what other nickname?

....

135. True or false? Rodney once took tap dancing lessons.

....

136. According to Del, England gave the world its three greatest sailors: Nelson, Drake and...?

....

137. According to Del, what couldn't Trigger find his way out of?

....

138. What was the name of Albert's wig wearing naval skipper?

....

139. What is Denzil's wife's name?

....

140. Which of Del's associates used to live in Cathle's House?

....

141. According to Rodney what would Del come up wearing if he fell into a viper's pit?

....

142. According to Rodney, where does Del get most of his French phrases from?

....

143. What is the name of the second hand car dealership Boycie owns?

....

144. Which of Del's associates has an uncle who lives in Outer Mongolia?

....

145. Which Driscoll brother does Del claim is "the brains of the outfit"?

....

146. When a guru predicted the world would end in a month, which Driscoll brother bet a grand that it would?

....

147. According to a favourite saying of Del's, what will the Trotters be "This time next year"?

....

148. Sid once had a job as what kind of driver?

a) Cab driver
b) Bus driver
c) Train driver ....

149. Which cousin of Del and Rodney sent Uncle Albert to Sainsbury's while she emigrated?

....

150. According to Del, Albert was once entertainment officer on which famous ship?

....

151. According to Albert, which old film star did his wife look like when he first met her?

....

152. Which old film star did she look like when he last saw her?

....

153. According to Del, his dad couldn't get a job because he suffered from what?

....

154. According to Del, what do the initials GLC stand for?

....

155. How many children does Elsie Partridge have?

....

156. What is the surname of the Trotters' short sighted neighbour, Clayton?

....

157. According to Danny Driscoll, what did his dad hang himself with?

....

158. Where was the post office in which Freddie the Frog accidentally killed himself?

....

159. What was the name of the explosives expert who died along with Freddie?

....

160. What was the name of the ship on which Albert spent his birthday in 1941?

....

161. What was the name of the American Aircraft carrier that Albert crashed into?

....

162. What, according to Rodney, is Sid's Cafe more affectionately known as?

....

The Official Only Fools and Horses Quiz Book

163. According to Boycie, what now stands on the sight of the Earl of Peckham's castle?

....

164. What American sport does Del refer to as "silly boys rounders"?

....

165. What part of London is Freddie the Frog from?

....

166. What part of London is Boycie from?

....

167. In which episode does Sid first appear?

....

168. In which episode does Cassandra first appear?

....

169. According to Rodney, his earliest memory of Del is of him standing in front of what?

....

170. Who said it? "The way you were talking we were gonna do a deal with Weetabix!"

....

171. Who said it? "He's been firing more blanks than the territorials!"

....

172. Who said it? "That's the way the cookie bounces".

....

173. Who said it? "For a minute I thought you said you loved me!"

....

174. Who said it? "Swivel on that, camel breath!"

....

175. Who said it? "Make those lagers long and cool"

....

176. Who said it? "Can you smell onions?"

....

177. Who said it? "I think in her own way she loved me. She never used to charge me as much as the other lads"

....

178. Who said it? "What've you got; a Wendy house?"

....

179. Who said it? "It's easier to sell bigger bananas than little ones"

....

180. Who said it? "They promised us homes fit for heroes. They give us heroes fit for homes"

....

181. Who said it? "Some people get wise men bearing gifts. We get a wally with a disease!"

....

182. Who said it? "I've got this feeling that he's haunting me. D'you know what I mean?"

....

QUIZ TEN- GENERAL KNOWLEDGE

183. Who said it? "Ain't this coach fitted with a fire distinguisher?"

....

184. Who said it? "It's amazing aint it, everything you buy off him has got something missing!"

....

185. Who said it? "We had an agreement. I do the thinking. You don't"

....

186. Who said it? "I've got this horrible feeling that if there is such a thing as reincarnation, knowing my luck I'll come back as me"

....

187. Who said it? "I've told you once Rodney, I won't tell you again son, I do the one, two, three, fours!"

....

188. Who said it? "At this pacific moment in time, we are a bit knackered for space"

....

189. Who said it? "Running away only wears out your shoes"

....

190. Who said it? "How the hell am I gonna persuade them that my grandad was Louis Armstrong?!"

....

191. Who said it? "In thirty five seconds you two have married me, buried me and given my widow skin trouble!"

....

192. Who said it? "Don't get any ketchup down your shirt"

....

193. Who said it? "Look out Margate and lock up your daughters"

....

194. Which of Del's associates was once caught speeding down Streatham High Street in a knocked off JCB?

....

195. Who, according to Del, cheered when Bambi's mum died?

....

196. Who is Del's favourite artist?

....

197. According to Del, what type of competitions did Rodney win a lot of when he was younger?

....

198. What did Del say he preferred when asked his thoughts on Hamlet?

....

199. Del once convinced who that they had one half a million pounds on the pools?

....

200. According to Denzil, who is the whitest man he has ever seen?

....

★ ★ ★

1. a) 2
2. Trotters Ethnic Tours
3. Croydon
4. Origami
5. Women in uniforms
6. Sidney Poitier
7. Harry Belafonte
8. Harris
9. b) San Francisco
10. b) 2
11. Bobby Finch
12. Caribbean Stallion
13. Half a lager
14. Vauxhall Velox
15. Janice
16. Bra
17. Don
18. b) A steak meal
19. Joycie
20. a) wealth
21. An Indian wicket keeper
22. Paving stones
23. Briefcases
24. b) Replay
25. Cheeseburger
26. b) £2,000
27. £17
28. b) The Monte Carlo Club
29. Earl
30. c) antibiotics
31. Shanghai Lil
32. Hong Kong
33. 3 weeks
34. They're men/transvestites
35. His false teeth
36. Air Hostess
37. Bus Conductress
38. Life insurance
39. c) America
40. Draughts
41. TIT
42. Giblets
43. The plug
44. The New Forest
45. The roof of Nelson Mandela House

46. Hong Kong

47. Stoke Newington

48. Shangri-La

49. A car / E-type Jaguar

50. George

51. Astroturf

52. Nocturnal Security Officer

53. b) Traffic Warden's uniform

54. Veronica

55. Skippy

56. Body Language, The Lost Art

57. Mickey Pearce

58. Oddjob

59. a) Michelangelo

60. Nero

61. Turkeys

62. Monica

63. Mickey Pearce

64. 4 minute warning

65. Eric

66. Wayne

67. Professional tennis player

68. Hot Rod

69. Cigar pack

70. Pork scratchings

71. Dust chute

72. Food poisoning

73. Skippy

74. Vimal Malik

75. Aunty Rose

76. c) Clacton

77. Corned beef

78. A pigeon

79. 1½ days

80. c) The circus

ANSWERS: QUIZ TWO - SERIES TWO

1. b) His teeth

2. Yves Saint Dior

3. c) Benidorm

4. b) Spanish omelette

5. Ridgemere Hall

6. b) Canaletto

7. c) Wallace

8. Old Shep

9. a) Monkey Harris

10. Abdul

11. Nylon tights

12. By taking empty bottles back

13. £4.37

14. Golden Lotus

15. a) Mr Chin

16. c) Blue

17. Luminous yellow

18. Trigger

19. a) Old Oak Cafe

20. c) Fried slice

21. Sid

22. Hotel Las Palmas

23. Alice

24. a) 40

25. 23½

26. Tommy Mackay

27. Parkhurst

28. c) ABH

29. b) French

30. c) Jackie

31. b) Persil

32. c) Policewoman

33. 12th March 1964

34. It's made of fibre glass

35. c) 1936

36. Gun-running

37. The Exterminator

38. a) 4

39. A mink coat

40. c) Louis 14th

41. Walking On The Moon

42. A double headed coin

43. Road sweeper

44. Grandad

45. In the telephone

46. a) £500

The Official Only Fools and Horses Quiz Book

47. Vic

48. A department store Father Christmas

49. Marlene

50. c) Gin and tonic

51. b) Doner kebab

52. Ireland

53. Mickey Pearce

54. a) The Magaluf Brothers

55. 4U2P

56. Brian

57. Traffic cone

58. How Much Is That Doggy In The Window?

59. b) Yeovil

60. c) North Korea

61. His car

62. A bowling green

63. We Three Kings Of Orient Are

64. Marcus

65. a) BBC 2

66. 4 aces

67. Zoe

68. Roller disco

69. a) Heathrow

70. Brixton

71. St Katherine's Dock

72. A cement mixer

73. b) Tarifa

74. Going down the slide backwards

75. b) Fog

76. Tails

77. b) Peking

78. b) Darren

79. Jay walking

80. c) Planetarium

218

SERIES
★★★★★★★★★★
THREE

1. Basil / Baz
2. Rodney
3. Boycie's
4. Salmon
5. Tregower
6. Trigger
7. Davenport
8. Chelsea
9. Harry
10. Broken lawnmower engines
11. Del
12. c) Alfie Flowers
13. Come On Eileen
14. c) Lassie
15. a) 'b'
16. Dr Becker
17. b) Nijinsky
18. Mickey Pearce
19. Pink
20. b) Jam sponge
21. Monopoly
22. Oranges
23. The Zoo
24. Del Boy's

25. Axe
26. b) Monkey Harris
27. Prince William
28. c) Burma
29. L. Lombardi Pets
30. Louis
31. Arturo
32. £45
33. £50
34. Benidorm
35. c) Crossroads
36. Queen Anne
37. Queen Elizabeth II
38. The Dukes Of Hazard
39. Haddock Pie
40. Blossom
41. a) A doctor
42. A bet
43. b) Oranges
44. Detective Inspector
45. c) West
46. Star Of Bengal
47. Rita Aldridge
48. b) Curry

49. Ghandi's revenge

50. Rorke's Drift

51. Cigarette case

52. c) Dan Tempest

53. The bloke that walked the plank

54. Mario's

55. Del Boy

56. The Peckham Pouncer

57. Margaret

58. Choreographer

59. Tom Witton

60. Asthma

61. a) Newcastle

62. Towser

63. Ginger Ted

64. b) Canada

65. Chief Robson

66. A Tin opener

67. Tank room

68. Marijuana

69. A smack in the face

70. O'Shaughnessy

71. Battleship grey

72. Gin

73. Mexican

74. Snooker

75. Sylvester

76. Barratts

77. Huddlestone's

78. She stole it

79. Joshua Blythe

80. c) His Richard Clayderman LP

81. Gambling

82. Karen

83. c) The kebab house

84. A strawberry

85. Fisher

SERIES
★ ★ ★ ★ ★ ★ ★ ★ ★
FOUR

1. b) Newsagents
2. A snake
3. c) Frankie Goes To Hollywood
4. Zebedee
5. DIY haircutting kit
6. c) Great Dane
7. Duke
8. c) £600
9. Solly Atwell
10. a) Bus
11. Maguire
12. Rampton
13. Louvre doors
14. Sausage and mash
15. Jamaican Swallowtail
16. Greenwich
17. £3,000
18. A dirty magazine
19. b) Wight
20. b) The Seychelles
21. The Vicar's
22. a) Jason
23. Denzil

24. Boomerang Trotter
25. Drums
26. Suntan lotion
27. 1965
28. c) Zimbabwe House
29. c) Salmonella
30. Tony Jacklin
31. Helga
32. c) Hamburg
33. Nine
34. A Bunch Of Wallies
35. Boys Will Be Boys
36. 26
37. Railway lines
38. Deidre
39. c) Bombay
40. Cigarette machine
41. Del Boy
42. I'm In The Mood For Love
43. a) 1 day
44. The Ferret
45. On an oil rig
46. Watches

The Official Only Fools and Horses Quiz Book

47. 50p

48. c) Aikido

49. The Shamrock Club

50. Liam

51. The Dublin Bay Stormers

52. c) 5 times

53. c) Duran Duran

54. Paddy The Greek

55. At Deidre's

56. c) Stan and Jean

57. Deep fat fryer

58. Yvonne

59. Showbusiness

60. a) 19th

61. Albie Littlewood

62. a) 15

63. Mickey Pearce

64. His neck

65. Alopecia

66. St Katherine's

67. Rodney

68. Denzil

69. Grapes

70. b) Eagle

71. His memory

72. Grandad

73. Sheena Easton

74. Uncle Albert

75. The cemetery

1. German
2. Swedish
3. Redhill
4. Mickey Pearce
5. Top Buys
6. b) £1,000
7. Patel's Multimart
8. Uncle Albert
9. Rodney
10. Mickey Pearce
11. Cars
12. c) 14 hours
13. Car cleaner
14. a) The Star of Bengal
15. c) Hampshire
16. c) His Cliff Richard cassette
17. The One Eleven Club
18. Ada
19. Night Nurse
20. a) St Mary's
21. Darts match
22. c) £185,000
23. c) Samantha Fox
24. Au pair
25. There Is A Rhino Loose In The City
26. Tom Clarke
27. c) Kenya
28. A nervous disorder
29. b) Trigger and Mike
30. c) Trumpet
31. Dimchurch
32. Boris Becker
33. Helen
34. b) Linda Evans
35. c) 6ft 6
36. Sunbed / home solarium
37. a) Smoking
38. Amanda
39. Mills
40. b) Australia
41. a) Fish stall
42. NOMAD
43. b) £29.48
44. c) Brut
45. c) Kipper

The Official Only Fools and Horses Quiz Book

46. Cheese

47. Spencer Wainwright

48. Vorsprung durch Technik

49. Lead from the church roof

50. b) Sunglasses Ron and Paddy The Greek

51. The Driscoll Brothers

52. b) Mark

53. Queen Victoria

54. c) The T and A

55. c) Mr Peterson

56. c) Entrecote Rioja

57. c) Valerie

58. Girl

59. Biffo the Bear

60. His Niece

61. Winchester

62. a) 25

63. a) Miss 999

64. c) Andy

65. a) £60,000

66. c) 46th

67. b) A Luger

68. The supermarket's toy department

69. b) 20th

70. c) The Shadow

71. Lennox Gilby

72. Paratroopers

73. c) Stevens

74. Seventh Heaven

75. Boycie

1. Gordon Gekko
2. The One Eleven Club
3. Otto
4. b) £2,000
5. Marble Arch At Dawn
6. Arc de Triumphe
7. a) Mallorca
8. Tomatoes
9. Bathroom
10. Mountbatten Estate
11. Pepsi and Shirley
12. Guernsey
13. Highcliff Hotel
14. b) Denzil
15. 7
16. His Dad
17. Jimmy Saville
18. Nerys
19. b) 14
20. Mobile phone aerial
21. Pork pie
22. 50
23. Dirty Barry
24. Spin dryer
25. b) Lusty Linda and Erotic Estelle
26. Chinese
27. c) Desmond Tutu House
28. A learner sign
29. b) Propane
30. Lee Harvey Oswald
31. Alan Perkins
32. Carmen
33. Play Things
34. Harrods
35. Brandy
36. Transworld Express
37. A doctor
38. Computerisation
39. Charlton
40. b) 2nd
41. A lizard
42. 6
43. a) Denzil
44. Trigger's
45. a) £36.24
46. c) 250

47. Beaujolais Nouveau '79

48. Robbie Meadows

49. Irritable Bowel Syndrome / IBS

50. £2.50

51. Formosa

52. Lady In Red

53. Elsie Partridge

54. b) China Gardens

55. Blackheath

56. DIC

57. Bay City Rollers

58. The Incredible Hulk's

59. Simone

60. A bag of liver

61. Maxi Stavros

62. Mr Jamil

63. The Groovy Gang

64. a) Eric Clapton

65. She is pregnant

66. Jewellery dealer

67. Pat

68. c) Steven and Gary

69. Jevon

70. A bacon sandwich

71. The Tower of London

72. Green Parrot disease

73. Dry clean only

74. Trudy

75. Bros

76. b) Mickey Pearce and Jevon

77. The Kings Avenue

78. Aubrey

79. a) The Who

80. Alan / Cassandra's Dad

81. His Stepmum

82. Emma

83. He's getting married

84. Italian

85. b) Mega Flakes

86. The Down By The Riverside Club

87. Petula

88. His filofax

89. b) Tandoori Nights

90. Rodney

91. Monkey Harris

92. Ghostbusters

93. Pork pie

94. Dr Shaheed

95. Condoms

96. Break dancing

97. a) Prince

98. One million Pesetas

99. His name

100. c) £3,000

1. Exchange and Mart
2. DEL 1
3. Policeman
4. Towser
5. c) Class 4C
6. Martin Luther King Comprehensive
7. Dockside Secondary Modern
8. Bend over Benson
9. Marlene's
10. Hampton Court Palace
11. Bronco
12. Brother-in-law
13. The Starlight Rooms
14. Eugene McCarthy
15. The SAS
16. Lil
17. Eric
18. c) As You Like It
19. Rosalind
20. Adrian
21. Agatha Christie
22. Knock-knock
23. Betty Ford
24. c) Mike
25. a) France
26. b) 12
27. Singing
28. Romania
29. Sigourney
30. Rodney
31. The Hotel Schubert
32. Colchester
33. Policeman
34. Elvis
35. Luxury Detached Abode
36. Low Demand Accommodation
37. Belly ache
38. 6
39. 4
40. a) Spain
41. A clip-on pony tail
42. A mouse
43. Jeremy Beadle
44. b) Parkhurst
45. Jesus

46. An undertaker

47. Trudy

48. Oily Olly

49. Undercover policemen

50. b) Lion

51. Ninja Turtles

52. The Down By The Riverside Club

53. Dustman

54. b) Midfield

55. Goalkeeper

56. c) Monkey Harris

57. Bamber Gascoigne

58. c) Gatwick

59. Tubby Fox

60. Barry Manilow

61. Crying

62. The Green Green Grass of Home, Congratulations or Please Release Me

63. Pronounciationism

64. Chernobyl

65. b) 2nd

66. A wig

67. b) America

68. A chipolata sandwich

69. Rachel

70. Henry

71. a) £50

72. b) Manchester

73. The Jesse Jackson Memorial Hall

74. Wapping

75. Greenshield stamps

76. Crowning Glory

77. Mustapha

78. Jules

79. a) 7 years

80. b) Ford Capri

81. a) Green

82. The Pratmobile

83. c) £400

84. Knock-knock

85. Fly-pitching

1. Imogen
2. Rajah
3. c) Carlotti's
4. Paintings
5. The Milan School of art and The Sorbonne
6. Covington House
7. Ear infection
8. b) Chief Detective Inspector
9. It's white wine
10. Romania
11. The Arch Bishop of Canterbury
12. Lorry driver
13. Technomatch
14. Bus conductor
15. His beard
16. Ruby
17. Indonesia
18. Chief mourner
19. Jevon
20. Nerys Sampson
21. Nervous Nerys
22. Musta F80

23. Albania
24. Kylie Minogue
25. Michelle
26. Luke's
27. The back of Denzil's lorry
28. c) Austria
29. b) £250,000
30. Alfred Broderick
31. Little Joe
32. Trivial Pursuit
33. Bic
34. Richard Branson
35. b) The dark
36. £1
37. b) Maylebury
38. c) Patterson
39. Roman Galley
40. Eddie Chambers
41. c) Sheffield
42. America
43. My Fair Lady
44. Dockside Cafe
45. b) £15,000

The Official Only Fools and Horses Quiz Book

46. Limpy Lionel

47. b) Carmen

48. Snell

49. b) Ronnie Nelson

50. a) The Hilton

51. c) Stephen

52. c) Joanne

53. Fergal Sharkey

54. They were little

55. a) Alligator

56. Inge

57. Hampshire

58. b) 13

59. Denzil

60. b) The Chain

61. Rico

62. A Sombrero

63. Berkshire

64. Hansome Samson

65. £10,000

66. A watch

67. Infrared massager

68. Sunny Sea Guest House

69. a) Mrs Baker

70. Denzil

71. The Villa Bella

72. Mrs Cresswell

73. Inga

74. The Middle East

75. Ajax

76. Harry

77. Denzil

78. Terry

79. Frog spawn

80. Blue Stratos

81. The Kid Jensen show

82. At sea

83. It's counterfeit

84. Sunglasses Ron, Paddy The Greek or Monkey Harris

85. Nervous breakdown

86. James Dean

87. The Great Ramondo

88. a) Barry Gibb

89. c) How Deep Is Your Love?

90. Hendrick

91. The Masons

92. b) Kent

93. a) The Parish Church of Peckham

94. Mickey Pearce

95. Hussein

96. Alan / Cassandra's Dad

97. 714 - 939

98. Mickey Pearce

99. Alberto Vasquez

100. The flame on his lighter

101. Mr Biggerstaff

102. His inflatable dolphin

103. Tanya

104. Honey I Shrunk The Kids

105. b) Eastbourne

106. Gatwick

107. The Mardi Gras

108. A football

109. Curry

110. 30

111. a) Cuba

112. AMRO

113. c) Pump-action shotgun

114. 'Iggy 'Iggins

115. Duval

116. Stephen / Cassandra's boss

117. An owl

118. Salvatore

119. a) £1,000

120. Herrington Road

121. Parker

122. Mike

123. Lurch

124. c) Margate

125. Calvin

126. b) Bull dog

127. Tennis

128. The Bear

129. A Concorde

130. Uncle Albert

CHRISTMAS SPECIALS
★★★★★★★★★★
1992 - 2003

1. Gary
2. Vasectomy
3. Albert's pants
4. a) Latvia
5. Lenny Norris
6. Monkey Harris
7. a) Slovakia
8. Mike
9. c) Boob job
10. One Voice
11. Ski gear
12. Grandad's
13. A Roman gladiator
14. A policewoman
15. Monkey Harris
16. A vampire
17. Spud-u-like
18. Tubular Bells
19. An Environmental Hygienist
20. A rabbit
21. Roger
22. Denzil
23. Trotters' Crash Turbans

24. Ziggy Sawdust
25. Coffee
26. Denzil's
27. Deep sea diver's outfit
28. Mont Chernobyl
29. Elsie Partridge
30. c) 20
31. b) 17 new heads and 14 new handles
32. Harrison
33. A Victorian egg timer
34. Goldrush
35. Jonathon Ross
36. Marlene
37. Peckham Spring
38. Cassandra
39. The 121 Club
40. b) Ronnie Nelson
41. b) Miguel
42. c) Rolls Royce
43. 1 DEL
44. Denzil and Trigger
45. a) 2026

46. Mickey Pearce

47. Nature's Way

48. Miles

49. c) Monte Carlo

50. Hotel de Paris

51. Modern Man

52. c) Ronnie Nelson

53. a) Russia

54. a) Brighton

55. The Grand

56. A sex machine

57. Gary

58. Justin

59. Cassandra's urine sample

60. HMS Cod

61. Sainte Claire de la Chapelle

62. White beards

63. George Parker

64. Hairs

65. Double Glazing Salesman

66. Burger King

67. Piles

68. Dr Singh

69. The Turbanator

70. a) 1983

71. Chicken Trotter

72. Trigger and Denzil

73. Onion puree

74. c) Sotheby's

75. b) £6.3 million

76. Harry Trotter

77. Princess Khadija

78. a) Gerbil

79. Gerry

80. A rat

81. Mike

82. Electric paint strippers

83. Sid

84. Harry Malcolm

85. Crown and Anchor

86. Batman and Robin

87. c) The Blues Brothers

88. The Lone Ranger and Tonto

89. A chauffeur

90. A backscratcher

91. Beverly

92. Boycie

93. An identity bracelet

94. Rooney

95. Prince Charles and Lady Diana's

96. Denzil

97. Barbados

98. c) Toothache

99. Snooker

100. Uncle Albert's Urn

101. Grandad's allotment

102. Rodney and Cassandra

103. Freddie the Frog

104. £145,000

105. Joan

The Official Only Fools and Horses Quiz Book

QUIZ TEN

★ ★ ★ ★ ★ ★ ★ ★ ★ ★

GENERAL KNOWLEDGE

1. Oxford
2. Brother
3. Ada
4. Big Brenda
5. Some soldiers
6. Turpin
7. Robdal
8. Brief Encounter
9. El Del
10. The plague
11. Louise
12. Tyler
13. Roddy
14. Eels on Wheels
15. a) Milton Keynes
16. b) Spain
17. 81
18. Bronco
19. Painter and Decorator
20. Paranoia
21. Lane
22. Printing
23. A Slow Boat To China
24. b) Del
25. c) Mike
26. 13
27. Dora
28. Tobacco Road
29. b) Rodney and Cassandra
30. c) Denzil
31. 3½
32. A beard
33. UK Gold
34. c) 9 lbs
35. A whale
36. Look after your broom
37. Antique dealer
38. Ugandan Maurice
39. Trigger
40. a) James and Audrey
41. Ghandi
42. Spanish
43. Peckham
44. Go West Young Man

45. The 3rd

46. A Chance Of A Lunchtime

47. 3

48. May The Force Be With You and Dates

49. May The Force Be With You and The Jolly Boys' Outing

50. It Never Rains and May The Force Be With You

51. A horse

52. Dougie Saddler

53. Millwall

54. Our Lady Of The Divine Rosemary

55. b) Two

56. Yellow

57. John Player Special

58. Abdul

59. Dr Becker

60. Daffodil

61. Roy Slater

62. His sister

63. Marilyn

64. Adam Faith

65. Albie Littlewood

66. Hampshire

67. Ronnie Nelson

68. Charlton Athletic

69. Her thigh

70. Absent

71. Who's A Pretty Boy?

72. True

73. False

74. True

75. False

76. Sleeping Dogs Lie

77. Nelson Mandela House

78. c) 12th

79. 3

80. Blue

81. Yellow

82. Ron's Cash 'n Carry

83. b) Alan and Pam

84. Christopher

85. Mavis

86. Mrs Oboko

87. Uncle Jack

88. Dave

89. Slater

90. True

91. True

92. c) New York, Paris, Peckham

93. b) The Kings Avenue

94. Gladstone

95. c) Maths and Art

96. False

97. Bus driver

98. b) Derek

99. Alex

100. Gods and Doctors

101. Betting shop

102. A tattooist

The Official Only Fools and Horses Quiz Book

103. Lenny Corby
104. c) 4th
105. An elephant
106. Basingstoke
107. For smoking marijuana
108. His Uncle George
109. c) 5
110. Carl
111. c) Lambeth
112. The Indictment
113. Dirty Barry
114. b) Del Boy
115. Rimini
116. Menthol
117. False
118. a) Harry and Ruby
119. b) 19
120. a) 17
121. Turner
122. Doctor Who
123. Double Cream
124. Nobby Clarke
125. His Father
126. Nelson Mandela
127. False
128. Maureen
129. Tea cosies
130. Mrs Murphy
131. The Nags Head
132. His Grandmother
133. The Peckham Echo
134. The Raffles Of Peckham
135. True
136. Columbus
137. Phone box
138. Captain Kenworthy
139. Corinne
140. Tommy Razzle
141. Snake skin shoes
142. A Citroen manual
143. Boyce Autos
144. Abdul
145. Danny Driscoll
146. Danny Driscoll
147. Millionaires
148. b) Bus driver
149. Audrey
150. The Belgrano
151. Ginger Rogers
152. Fred Astaire
153. A sticky mattress
154. General 'lectric Company
155. 11
156. Cooper
157. His braces
158. Plumstead
159. Jelly Kelly
160. HMS Peerless
161. USS Pittsburgh
162. The Fatty Thumb
163. The Kwik Fit Exhaust Centre
164. Baseball

Answers: Quiz Ten - General Knowledge

165. Rotherhithe
166. Lewisham
167. The Long Legs Of The Law
168. Yuppy Love
169. A mirror
170. Mickey Pearce
171. Marlene
172. Uncle Albert
173. Del
174. Rodney
175. Jevon
176. Boycie
177. Uncle Albert
178. Grandad
179. Del Boy
180. Grandad
181. Del Boy
182. Denzil

183. Trigger
184. Boycie
185. Danny Driscoll
186. Rodney
187. Mental Mickey
188. Del Boy
189. Del Boy
190. Boycie
191. Rodney
192. Cassandra
193. Rodney
194. Bronco
195. Boycie
196. Van Gogh
197. Ugly bird competitions
198. Costello's
199. Grandad
200. Rodney

How Did You Do....?

You scored

Quiz One - Series One	out of 80
Quiz Two - Series Two	out of 80
Quiz Three - Series Three	out of 85
Quiz Four - Series Four	out of 75
Quiz Five - Series Five	out of 75
Quiz Six - Series Six	out of 100
Quiz Seven - Series Seven	out of 85
Quiz Eight - Christmas Specials (1985 - 1991)	out of 130
Quiz Nine - Christmas Specials (1992 - 2003)	out of 105
Quiz Ten - General Knowledge	out of 200

900 - 1015	Crème De La Menthe
800 - 900	42 carat diamond
700 - 800	Lovely Jubbly
600 - 700	Cushty
500 - 600	Cosmic
400 - 500	Maybe this time next year

300 - 400	Have you been on the Moroccan woodbines?
200 - 300	What's the weather like on planet dippy?
100 - 200	You dozy Twonk!
0 - 100	Is your name Trigger?

More from
Splendid Books

FREE DELIVERY ON ALL ORDERS

Compiled by Steve Clark, bestselling author of *The Only Fools and Horses Story*, and television expert Shoba Vazirani, *The British Television Location Guide* reveals the settings for dozens of top television shows.

From *Only Fools and Horses* to *Doc Martin* and from *Emmerdale* to *Doctor Who*, the book gives details of how you can visit the places you have seen so many times on the box. Just **£9.99**

Read the real story of life behind the scenes at *The Bill* by the show's Graham Cole, who played PC Tony Stamp, in this frank autobiography. £17.99 (hardback) or £7.99 (paperback)

Read actor Derek Martin's fascinating real East End life story from growing up during the Blitz to starring as Charlie Slater in *EastEnders*. £17.99 (hardback)

To order:

By phone: **0845 625 3045** *or online:* **www.splendidbooks.co.uk**

By post: Send a cheque (payable to Splendid Books Limited) to: Splendid Books Limited, The Old Hambledon Racecourse Centre, Sheardley Lane, Droxford, Hampshire SO32 3QY